CW00664012

Outside of a dog . . .

OUTSIDE OF A DOG...

an anthology of new writing

INTRODUCTION BY ALAN BISSETT

First Published 2006
by CHROMA
an imprint of Black & White Publishing Ltd
99 Giles Street, Edinburgh EH6 6BZ

ISBN 13 978 1 84502 101 6
ISBN 10 184502 101 0

Introduction copyright © Alan Bissett 2006
Stories, poetry and extracts copyright © the authors, 2006
The Contributors Notes on pages 273 to 277
constitute an extension of this copyright notice.

All rights reserved. No part of this publication may be
reproduced, stored in a retrieval system, or
transmitted in any form, or by any means, electronic,
mechanical, photocopying, recording or otherwise,
without permission in writing from the publisher.

A CIP catalogue record for this book is
available from the British Library.

The Publisher acknowledges subsidy from the Scottish
Arts Council towards the publication of this volume.

With support from Glasgow City Council

Typeset by RefineCatch Limited, Bungay, Suffolk
Printed and bound by Nørhaven Paperback A/S

ACKNOWLEDGEMENTS

Our thanks go to Alan Bissett and Michael Schmidt.

The coordinators of this anthology were
George Anderson, Alison Irvine, Katy McAulay,
Andrea McNicoll, Allan Radcliffe and Mary Smith.

Dedicated to Willy Maley, gentleman and scholar.

Contents

INTRODUCTION

It was 2004 and I was in Leeds. I knew no writers except the university students whom I taught, and I was teaching too many of them. Work on the second book had been crawling along. And it was all kicking off in Glasgow. I'd bumped into the newly published Louise Welsh and Zoë Strachan at the 2002 Edinburgh Book Festival. Anne Donovan's *Buddha Da* was everywhere in 2003, having been shortlisted for yet another award. There was Rachel Seiffert on *Granta*'s prestigious 20 Best Young Writers list in the same year. In 2004 I met with an excited young man named Rodge Glass, shortly after his book deal. And who was this Laura Marney, whose first novel, *No Wonder I Take a Drink*, was performing miracles in bookstores? I'll raise you a Colette Paul, a Nick Brooks, a Will Napier. They all had debuts on the way. I was in Leeds and staggered by what had begun in Glasgow since I'd left Scotland two years before. Having set up camp in the new decade and in the one place, there were all these young writers suddenly on the rise, and so much of it seemed down to a single significant factor: the MLitt in Creative Writing at the University of Glasgow. It was producing success stories with alarming regularity, and the appointment of James Kelman, Alasdair Gray and Tom Leonard as joint

Professors of Creative Writing had created tremors in the annals of academia which reached me even down south. I had to get back up there. As a young Scottish writer myself it was the only place to go. I buttonholed the course convenor, Willy Maley, in an Edinburgh cafe and gave him my pitch. He had fifteen minutes, leaving as he was for a party, at which he would help push Alison Miller towards her eventual publisher, Penguin. A few months later I found myself teaching on the course alongside Zoë Strachan, Laura Marney and two of Glasgow's literary greats, Janice Galloway and Tom Leonard. The energy, the convergence of talents, both established and new, that were at work in and beyond the uni community was something completely unrecognisable from my ascetic seclusion in Leeds. *Aye Write!*, the inaugural Glasgow Book Festival, took place in 2004, and tempted William McIlvanney into reading new work for the first time in years. There were exciting writers everywhere on and around the course; the students were brimming with quality. Sorting through the hundred or so applicants for the 2005–06 year proved difficult when every one of them seemed so good.

Here are the successful students – sorry, *writers* – from that crop. If Glasgow has, this decade, been a magnet for new writing talent in Scotland, this book represents a stunning single year's snapshot of it. I would be very surprised indeed if at least one of these names did not soon break through and themselves contribute to the ever-changing perception of Glasgow literature as one of supposedly dour, industrial laments (an image never really more than shorthand or stereotype) to something truly diverse, inclusive, varied and unpredictable. A charge often falsely levelled at creative writing courses is that they encourage a sausage-factory aesthetic, a certain style, safety and sensibility. That's clearly pish. It may be possible to liken all writers to others – there's a fascination here with the East from three of them, another three employ dialect, more than a few have a great deal to say about love and its discontents – but that's more because of the universality of certain big subjects than any designated movement or approach. A quick glance at the breadth of settings, voices and themes on display is enough to quell such fears. I'd be surprised if in any other collection you'd find side by side the inner lives of gannets, the sex lives of gangsters, and the coming of a second Ice Age in Glasgow.

Anneliese Mackintosh, startlingly, manages to look beyond her years into the sadness of ageing, the quiet retreat into infirmity and horror at what the body has become. Ewan Gault's piece, by contrast, is a restrained, hushed tale of adolescent misadventure, with a disquieting undertow. Like Gault, Kate Dowd writes in the vernacular, but hers is from the American Deep South, producing a ghost story in the tradition of Toni Morrison. Its warmth of voice offsets some chilling discoveries. John Mc Geown's piece is a cold, hard stare at a troubled relationship. Andrea McNicoll's writing is part of an international outlook frequently on show in this collection: the amorous goings-on in a Thai village are depicted with more affection and veracity than most writing about the East by Westerners. George Anderson's work, perhaps the most obviously 'Scottish' as that term is applied, gives the lie to the notion that comedy writing lacks depth and integrity; his hilarious brace of tales provide subtle commentary on such weighty topics as social inclusion and the nature of art. Kirsten Anderson's stories are about love and death and the dark, almost absurd, combination of the two. Fiona Bingham's whisper-quiet but heart-breaking tale about a husband being sent to war is accompanied by the volume's only non-fiction – a revealing piece of travel writing about the cult of Chairman Mao. Marie-Anne Mancio rolls in linguistic jokes, with her idiosyncratic, pointed and moving depiction of a lost love affair. Allan Radcliffe offers an unsettling depiction of a marriage suffering from chronic alcoholism, one which sends a shudder through the spine in its ending.

The poems too are multifaceted and surprising. Sara Bryce's are sensitive insights into snatched, stolen moments between lovers and friends. George Anderson wittily subverts Burns's 'To a Mouse'. Lorna Callery writes sharp, clever poems on seemingly intangible themes such as art. Maggie Walker's poems on nature are careful and luminous. Mary Smith writes searing verses protesting war. Theresa Muñoz arranges a sequence of poems on the life of Clara Schumann with stark, imagistic skill.

Lastly we find extracts from novels warming up to be potential future bestsellers. Eleanor Thom's is from Scotland's past, about a community shown rarely in fiction – that of travelling folk – and told with ironic insight by a young narrator. Vincent Wells's concerns a childhood humiliation, narrated with a poker-faced prose that defies the reader not to scream with laughter. Hannah Ritchie's brief, hurt-filled tale is about adolescent love, loss and betrayal. John Mc Geown's is a lively piece about an unravelling contretemps in a Dublin courtroom. Maggie Walker, summoning great sympathy for her narrator, takes us into the bitter-sweet terrain of school crushes and hopes dashed. The romantic travails in an Afghan community are the vehicle for a universal message from Mary Smith. Felix Boon's frankly hysterical story is about the world's worst wank. Alison Irvine writes with muted, Carver-esque precision on the flickerings of a love affair, and the threads of darkness which haunt its surface. Alastair Sim is in the Scottish thriller territory of Buchan and Rankin, investigating the dark heart of the military. Allison Deeds explores the aftermath of a car crash in the low tones of pathos. Ann Burnett's deft, light touch concerns a stultifying mother–daughter relationship, and an escape into a wild(ish) night out with the girls. Les Wood combines, with comic aplomb, the incongruous genres of sex farce and gangster thriller. Christin Lee offers a bold shot of Americana, whose prose is as fervent as the religious fanaticism it describes. Katy McAulay's piece is, oddly enough, the only one definitely about Glasgow, but it is a Glasgow transformed and made strange by a beauty rarely seen in the city's literature.

This is writing of fluidity and confidence, a must for anyone interested in glimpsing future stars of British literature. That it confirms Glasgow as a thriving literary capital is secondary; it confirms each individual as a writer excitedly in the ascendant, evolving towards an ever-clearer realisation of their ideas, hovering in their own moment before their art is borne into the wider world. This collection, for many of them, is where that first takes place. They are here and so are you. It's all still kicking off.

Alan Bissett
University of Glasgow Library,
March 2006

a book is a man's
best friend.

SHORT
STORIES

GRACE

ANNELIESE MACKINTOSH

She had not taken off her make-up for three days, but still nobody had come to the door. Grace sat at her walnut dressing table, and wrinkled her lips as she rubbed in a little more lipstick. A very pretty shade of pink, with a name like Hyacinth or Coral or . . . or something else that was pink, though she could not remember what. She had bought the lipstick years ago for a party. Everyone had commented on how good she had looked in her frock and feather boa and matching pink lips. A long time had passed since then, but she had found the lipstick in her medicine cabinet the other day, whilst looking for some aspirin, and she thought it might be just what she needed.

She dabbed the end of the lipstick on each cheek. A bit of rouge. As the lipstick passed under her nose it smelt thick and sticky, like the angel cake she had eaten on her wedding day. What lovely memories. If only she could remember them all. She puffed her lips out at the mirror to see how she looked. There. That was better. She had some colour again. Maybe just a little more black on her eyes and that would be it for now. She shut her eyes down hard on her black make-up brush, scraping her eyelids slightly. Her eyelashes weren't what they used to be, but a bit of paint sorted that out. She sucked in her cheeks and stuck out her lips to look at herself again. The sun behind her shone into the mirror and lit up her face. She felt years younger.

It looked like a fine day outside. Maybe someone would come by and take her for a picnic. She had not been on a picnic for years, but when she did she always took her green rug with her. It was soft, and it was the colour of grass. She would sit with her friends, and watch the children in the park play hide and seek. She would eat sweets and biscuits. She would lick the sugar off her chin, and she would laugh like a bird.

Thinking about it all made something growl in her stomach. How much had she eaten today? It was difficult for her to remember when she had last eaten anything at all. Trying to remember made her feel hungry.

She lifted herself up from her walnut chair, and tick-tacked her way in her pearly slippers to the kitchen. She opened a cupboard. Two tins of sardines. One jar of pickled cabbage. She opened the fridge. Shelled prawns. What should she eat? She did not feel like prawns today. What she really fancied was a big crumbly muffin. She used to treat herself to one every Saturday before the bakery on the corner closed down. But there was an estate agent's in its place now, so she couldn't eat anything there. Only Hansel and Gretel were foolish enough to eat houses. There was talk of another bakery, past the post office and on the other side of the square, but that was unfamiliar territory, and too far to travel for the sake of a muffin. She looked in the cupboard again, opening the door carefully, remembering the time the apple pie had fallen on her head. The sardines said they were in a rich tomato sauce. That sounded nice, but more like lunch than breakfast. She would have a cup of tea instead.

The kettle bubbled and blew. She looked into its shiny surface. There was a funny picture in it. 'Look at that!' she laughed. 'Look at me!' Then she noticed in the reflection that her nightgown was full of stains. She could not remember why the stains were there, but they made her sad.

POP! went the kettle. *Snap out of it.*

KNOCK! went the door. She jumped.

Two such sudden noises in a row. Especially the second one. It had been a long time since someone had knocked at her door.

She stepped into the hallway and blinked at the door suspiciously. Her eyelids hurt when she blinked. She tried to remember what you were supposed to say when somebody knocked at your door. 'Just a minute,' she tried, in a whisper. She tip-tapped back to her room. Her dressing gown was hanging on the back of her door. That would hide the stains.

Knock, went the door again. *Knock knock knock knock.*

'Just a minute,' she repeated, but the words didn't make a noise when they came out. She went over to her walnut dressing table and checked herself in the mirror. A pink satin gown hanging over a pot belly. Her stick-legs poked out at the bottom, covered in whiskery hair. She tried to pull the dressing gown down over her knees. Her fingernails caught on the satin. They were so brittle these days, like the seashells she had felt between her toes when Jim took her to the beach. A nail snapped and she decided to leave the gown as it was. But would that do? What if the person at the door laughed?

Rat-a-tat-tat. You look fat.

She put some more lipstick on and rubbed her lips together. Then pouted. Her nose had grown so big, sometimes it was all she could see when she looked at her face. But it would have to do. She walked towards the front door. Hurrying like this made her wheeze. She stopped to take a few quiet gulps of air. It was not a good idea to answer the door out of breath. Then she really would be laughed at. She got her breath back, took two more steps, and reached for the door handle.

Before she could turn it, a small card plopped down on to the mat and tickled her feet. She picked it up and read it aloud, like the first clue of a treasure hunt. 'We called to deliver a package at eight forty-three a.m. but you were out. Please call us to rearrange a delivery.' Next to where it said 'package', they had crossed out 'packet' and 'parcel'. How peculiar! Who would deliver a package to her? Deliver. Delivery. What slimy words.

We called.

You were out.

Please call us.

It was like a showing-off, a telling-off and an invitation all in one. Was it all true? They had called. Yes. But she was not out. So should she call them? Maybe she should write her own card and post it back through the letterbox.

You called.

I was not out.

Please call again.

She let the card drop back on to the mat. Her mouth was dry. She had still not had anything to drink. A cup of tea would help her think.

There was a greasy pink half-moon left on the rim of the cup after she took a sip. It was her favourite cup, that one. She always drank out of it. A coronation mug. It was getting old now of course. There was a chip at the top and it was starting to get a crack down one side. Jim had bought it for her.

He used to buy her a different cup every year. When they were courting, the cups had hearts and poems on them. When they were newly married, the cups got a bit more serious, in matching sets or with saucers, to go in their first home together. Then there were the cups for special occasions, like the coronation mug. That one was her favourite because he bought it for her during a trip to the seaside, on their first real holiday together. He said it was a souvenir, and even now it made her think of walking along the beach with him. But as Jim had got older, his eyes had started to go, and he gave her an employee of the month mug. And then his mind started to go, and he thought she worked for him.

Jim died eight years ago. On quiet days, when Grace was missing him too much, she poured herself a hot cup of tea in one of his mugs, and she warmed her hands on it as if it were his skin.

The mug was too hot to hold for long, though, not like Jim's warm back, which she used to hold all night long. She put it down. Some of the tea dribbled down the side, running down the queen's face and on to the sideboard. She thought about wiping it up, but the idea made her head hurt. It gave her a thumping headache. *Thump, thump.*

She realised it was the door. *Thump thump thump thump.*

Who could it be this time? Maybe it was the person with the package trying again. They might even come in for a cup of tea if asked nicely. She would just pop a bit more lipstick on then answer it. Most of it had come off on the teacup. She padded back to the bedroom.

'GRAN?' There was a voice coming through the letter-box. 'IT'S SAMANTHA. ARE YOU IN?'

Grace wiped some more lipstick across her mouth and retied the belt around her robe. It cut into her stomach. 'Just a minute!' she called faintly. Her throat felt slimy, like she needed to cough.

'GRAN, I'VE GOT TO BE QUICK. I CAN'T STOP. ON MY WAY TO CATCH THE BUS. I'VE GOT ANNA WITH ME. SHE JUST WANTED TO DROP OFF A PICTURE SHE'S DRAWN YOU.'

'Just a minute,' Grace repeated, coughing. Her grand-daughter could not see her like this. She might think she could not cope. She *could* cope. She would go out for a picnic by herself this afternoon. That was coping. She would have sweets and biscuits and sit on her green rug. It would be lovely.

She tugged off her nightgown, trying not to look down at her naked body.

'GRAN? I'VE GOT TO CATCH THE BUS IN A MINUTE.' The voice through the letterbox was urgent. It sounded frightening when it travelled down the hall like that.

She pulled a flowery pink dress out of her wardrobe, one that looked perfect for a picnic, and she dragged it over her skin. It was tight around the middle and it gaped at her breasts. She could see her nipples poking through it like raisins. But at least there were no stains on it.

'GRAN?'

I'm not deaf, she thought. I'm slow, but I'm not deaf.

'OH, I'VE GOT TO GO NOW, I CAN SEE THE BUS COMING UP THE HILL. I'LL PUT THE PICTURE THROUGH YOUR LETTERBOX. I'LL POP BY AGAIN SOON. BYE!'

Grace's throat looked too bare with her neck gaping like that. She reached into the back of her wardrobe and pulled out her pink feather boa. It was just like being back at the party. Samantha would like to see it. She used to let her play with it when she was a little girl. Maybe little Anna would like it too. It was made of real turkey feathers.

She walked into the hall, ready to be seen in her summer dress. Too late. There was a colourful piece of paper lying on the mat. Her second card today. It was like a birthday. It almost made her forget that she had missed the door. She went over to it and picked it up, and smiled at the red and blue scribbles and bits of tissue paper screwed up and glued on to it. The scribbles looked as if they might be some sort of secret code.

We called.

You were too slow.

We will call again. Soon.

She put the picture in her dress pocket. What was she to make of all this? She padded back towards the kitchen,

11

expecting to see something terrible or funny waiting for her in there. She thought of Jim. The way he had looked, standing there at the stove that day, wearing just a straw hat and a pair of soiled underpants, and stirring a saucepan of porridge. She remembered his toothless smile when he had asked where his mother was. And the shame when she could not think of an answer to give him.

There was nothing waiting for her in the kitchen today.

The saucepan was still empty, her cup was still chipped, and it still had tea in it. It was cooler now. She took a slurp.

The world was a very big place.

Next time, she thought. Next time I'll be ready.

It took her quite a while to do, but eventually she managed to set it out. Her green picnic rug at one end of the hall. Her walnut chair upon it, which she sat on, with a cup of cold tea in her hand. By her feet, for anybody who might join her, was a spare cup and a jar of pickled cabbage (she had no sweets or biscuits). And at the other end of the hall, in full view, was the front door.

Clutched in her free hand, sticky and melting, was her lipstick.

'I'm ready!'

And she waited.

A Hole in the Ice

Ewan Gault

Oor footsteps crunched in time through frozen snow, the only noise on a woolly-hat day. The camera Ah had got for Christmas bounced importantly on ma chest, heavy and useless. Ah sneaked a look at Ally's pinched face, cheeks sharpened by the falling snow. A penny for yir thoughts, Ah wanted tae say, but didn't.

'Do you fancy going up tae Paradise Pool?'

Ally shrugged, not a yes or a no. We followed the footprints up the road that the Forestry Commission had long since ceased to use. Ever grim, dull green trees, huddled in queues, wrapped tight in shawls and scarves of snow. It wis always a silent place, the trees planted too close together, waiting for harvesting.

'Do you think the water'll be frozen over?' Ah asked.

'Ma braer said it wis.'

'But will it be safe?'

'Dunno, Ah'll go first if yir feart.'

'Ah'm naw feart, jist wondering.'

We passed the sign warning about starting fires, a picture ay a startled deer running away fae the flames. Leaning against it were two wooden poles wi black rubber squares nailed to the end tae put out fires.

'Mind we used tae fight wi them?' Fighting wi Ally wisnae fun, naw like wi other people. Ally wis too quick and dangerous, didn't care if you got hurt. 'Ah cracked wan o yir teeth, didn't Ah?'

'Like tae see you try it now.' Ally shrugged. Ah felt pretty stupid, 'cause Ah wis much bigger than Ally these days, and, well, it widnae be right, not now. Ah looked at the big metal triangle wi its flaky red paint and rust. You were meant tae bang it tae warn folks about fires but Ally used tae use it like a bell fae a boxing match before wan ay oor fights. Ah wis always worried that the polis or fire brigade might come, but Ally wid jist laugh and clang it harder. Ah'd want tae leg it but we stayed put and nobody ever came, nobody heard a thing.

'Strike a pose,' Ah said, lifting the camera threateningly.

'Fuck off, Gordie.'

'Aww, jist wan picture.'

'You ken Ah dinnae like getting ma photay taken.'

Ah scuffed ma boots through the snow and looked aff at the tangled rhododendrons that marked the boundaries of the auld estate. When we were weans we used tae climb aw the way through the breathless centre of the bushes, trying naw tae touch the ground. Wance we found three old gravestones, hidden amongst the branches and leaves. Ah minded saying that no wan wid hae found these but us. They were much smaller than normal gravestones. Ah thought they were probably for animals, pets ay the folk that used tae live in the auld hoose. Ally hud jumped aff a branch, started clearing the pale dry leaves.

'There's no names, that's strange, isn't it?'

Ah hud shrugged. You could hear the rain crawling over the outside leaves. 'They were probably orphans.'

'Orphans?'

'Aye, they made the place into an orphanage fir a bit.'

Ally had crawled oot intae the real world and left me there. Came back wi a shower of snowdrops that we scattered around the gravestones.

We were nearly at the path leading aff tae Paradise Pool when Ah saw Ally's braer oot walking the dog, which wis about all he ever did since he hud dingied college. He came towards us wi his careless sloppy walk which Ah used tae try and copy.

'Whit are you two lovers up to?' He always called the two ay us lovers, jist tae wind Ally up. Ah kent that the best way tae avoid this wis jist tae ignore him but Ally couldn't.

'Shut the fuck up, Rory.'

He smirked at me, and Ah laughed back. It wis funny wi Rory at times, like we were in some big joke together against Ally.

'That a new camera?'

'Aye, Christmas present, it's a Polaroid.'

'Very nice,' Rory said, lifting the weight of the camera off ma chest. He examined it wi greedy eyes. Ah minded a time when Ah hud brought an archery set to Ally's and he hud come intae the gairden and snapped the bow. No reason, not a word. Me and Ally said nowt. Jist went and played wally, kicking the ball as hard as we could.

'Do you want your picture taken?'

'Aye, hold Laika's lead, Ally.' He raced off round the back ay a gorse bush. Ah couldnae see him for a bit but then his face appeared breaking through prickly branches. 'Hold on a bit,' he shouted, pulling his black woolly hat over his face. He let out a scream and Ah took the photo.

'You're crazy,' Ah sais as he untangled himself.

'Aye and don't you forget it. Come on then, how does it look?'

'Well you cannae really make anything out.'

'Oh, Ah like that. To anyone else a picture of a boring auld bush, but we know,' he sais, looking grim, 'we know there's a monster in there.'

Rory strode on up tae Paradise Pool, shouting instructions in his whiny voice. Ally gave me a look as if tae say, well, that's today's fun ruined, and we followed on up the path.

Laika wis tugging at his lead summit fierce and Ah told Ally Ah wid take him. He wis a big brute ay a dog, muscles bunched up round his collar as he chased and darted around a world of smells.

'Do you mind when Laika wis a puppy and you used tae ballroom dance wi him?'

Ally frowned.

'You must remember, you had scratches on yir shoulders all the time fae it.'

'Oh, aye, seems a long time ago.'

It wis funny that Ally wid forget summit like that 'cause it wis such a comic sight, the dog wi its forepaws on Ally's shoulders, its dumb slavering face looking about excited.

The pond wis frozen over right enough. Rotten logs and dirty barrels fae the summer's raft-building projects lay trapped in its hold. Ally wis set tae jist walk straight on out but Rory said tae wait. He picked up a boulder from the side and bounced it across the ice. It made the oddest sound, a deep, smearing resonance. Ally danced out over the pool. After the noise the rock made Ah almost wanted the ice tae crack, jist tae hear the noise of something break. The two ay them started charging aboot, seeing who could skid the furthest over a patch they hud cleared ay snow.

'Get yerself out here, Gordie.'

Ah let go of the dug's lead and skittered ontae the ice. It felt weird, like totally solid but you kent that not far beneath wis the dark cold water. Ally wis jumping and stamping on one part ay ice jist daring it tae break. 'It's totally solid.' We started throwing sticks fir Laika who chased after them, sliding all over the place when he tried tae stop.

'This is a laugh,' Ah said before jumping as Rory crunched a metal pole ontae the surface. 'Whit you doin?'

'Gonnae smash a hole through the ice tae see how deep it is.'

'Fair enough,' Ah sais, thinking, Whit the fuck? Anyhow Rory started smashing the pole intae the ice, holding it totally vertical so that only the point hit the ice. It felt strange through your feet, through your bones, a shivering echo.

'Gonnae gie us a go?' Rory handed the pole over. Ah wis desperate tae break through the ice, jist like pretending it wis fragile, pretending it wis solid. 'Fucker!' Ah shouted. 'Fucker!' It started cracking and Rory gave a whoop.

'Gie us it.'

Ah gave him back the pole, ma hands numb fae the effort. Wi wan mighty thump Rory thrust the pole through the ice, letting it sink into the depths. Dark, oily-looking water lapped over the edges as he started clearing away the broken ice. 'Dinnae get too close,' he barked at Ally who wis bouncing near the edge.

'Let's try and jump the hole.' Ah went first and then Ally. It wis easy, naw a big jump but still scary wi the water below. We did it a few times, pulling daft faces and shapes in the air.

'Make it bigger, Rory.' Ally caught the dog and got me tae put the lead on it. 'Come on, Laika, come on, boy. Wir gonnae jump across the hole in the ice.'

'He'll niver make it.'

'Aye he will!' Ally snapped. 'Won't you, Laika? Yir a big boy, you'll make it.' Looking at me, Ally sais, 'You can take that photo now if you want.'

As they started running Ah saw Rory's face sort ay crumple like somewan swallowing a scream. Ally jumped clean across the hole, landing neatly on the run. Laika leapt for all he wis worth but the dug's back end splashed heavily intae the water. He started pawing at the ice, panting wi girlish grunts. Ally wis laughing and pointing: 'Get a photay ay that.' Rory pulled the dug out, it stood there dripping and shaking.

'Whit the fuck did you do that for?' he shouted, his voice clenched tight.

'Jist fir a laugh,' Ally whispered, wide-eyed, mock serious.

'A laugh? You,' sais Rory, eyes flexing at me, 'did you think that wis funny?'

Ah shrugged. 'Aye, Ah suppose. Didnae hurt anywan, did it?'

'The two of you are mental. Mental in the heid.' We baith laughed, Ally giving me a strong look. It wis a gid moment, felt fir the first time the day like we were proper, like we were together. 'Well youse can go an find the dog yirselves. Ah'm naw chasin aftir it.'

We stormed aff. Laika hud run away up the firebreak between the trees. It wis hard goin wi auld broken branches an snow on the ground. There probably wisnae any point as the dug wisnae daft and Ah wis sure he'd make his own way back. Still Ah jogged on, eyes locked on Ally who wisnae getting away. Soon enough we stopped tae catch oor breath and see if we could hear anything.

'Ah'm flaked,' Ally wheezed. 'How wis the photay?' Ah'd managed tae press the button jist before they jumped. A picture ay an iced-over lake, a dark hole in it if you looked close enough. 'You really are a shite photographer, Gordie.'

Ah smiled at the ground and set off up the firebreak. Ah ran fast, for a moment feeling totally alone, imagining how that would be in this place in the gloaming. Ah ducked down tae look at the forest floor, an endless desert ay pine needles, occasional piece ay litter looking lost. The sound of Ally's ragged breathing caught up.

'It's starting tae get dark, Gordie. Ah dinnae think Laika's up here.'

'Jist a bit further and we come out on the forestry road.' Ah wis right. The trees opened out and we stumbled ontae a flat surface, each step seeming insanely easy after what we hud jist ran up. There wis an auld caravan at the edge ay the woods. Ah went and peered through the grimy windaes. The caravan must hae been ancient 'cause they were made ay glass an even oor caravan hud plastic windaes. The inside wis full ay old gas canisters, used tyres, that kind ay stuff. On the table at the far end were two plates, two mugs and an empty jam jar, a knife resting in it.

Ah tapped on the windae and shouted hello. Ah kent there wis no wan there bit Ah kind ay hud tae do it. Whin Ah turned round Ally wis holding a rock. 'Yir naw gonnae . . .' Ah started as the side windae shattered. Ah picked up a stick and dragged it around the windae frame, laughing with the tinkling glass. Ugly brown curtains flapped filthily in the air. Ally picked up a smaller rock and put in the next windae. Ah strolled round tae the back ay the caravan, swinging ma stick like a baseball bat, smashing it easily. We broke the other two side windaes the same way. It wis great, the feeling of waking up wi a start. Fir the big front windae, we lifted a log fae the side ay the road and charged with it like a battering ram. We hud done all the windaes now but Ah wisn't through and went round punching all the toothy bits wi ma thick winter gloves. Fir the last wan Ah took the gloves aff and punched the icy glass. Hot sticky blood dribbled between ma knuckles and Ah held ma arm above ma heid. It made me feel special that something so bright and warm had been inside me.

Ally opened the door and we peered in. There wis a familiar rotten smell about the place. Ah wis glad that the night's air wis cleaning it out. The jar wi the knife in it still had bits ay jam staining the glass.

'You got matches, Gordie? We'll light the curtains and the couch.' Ah nodded. They baith caught easy, like the fabric had jist been waiting fir somewan to put a match to it. We should really huv legged it but that didnae cross ma mind. All Ah wanted wis to stay and see the caravan go up in smoke, the whole world explode. Flames began flickering oot ay the broken windaes and soon we were standing knee deep in the fire's splashing light, our clothes sodden in its glow.

'Take a photay, Gordie.'

And Ah knew then that Ah should hae pointed the camera at Ally 'cause Ah hud niver seen anywan look so beautiful. Instead Ah took a picture of the howling fire, the shocked darkness behind the windaes. When Ah put the camera down Ah saw Rory standing at the end ay the fire-break. Ah dinnae ken how long he hud been there or what he hud seen. His face wis the colour of a ghost that could no longer haunt. He walked round the outside of the light, Laika at his side, whimpering and confused.

Ally smiled like she didn't care. Took off her woolly hat and threw it intae the flames. Her hair wis much longer these days and hud been cut in a grown-up fashion. She stood for a moment longer, her eyes in shadow from the light of the fire. She tilted her head back, letting the snow fall on her bare face, and stuck out her tongue to try and catch a flake. When this no longer interested her she turned tae walk home. We followed, two unsteady shadows on a winter's night. The snow would fall for hours, a constant hush across the land.

Midnight, Mississippi

Kate Dowd

It sho is hot in Mississippi round this time a year. It's s hot the gaters don even try ta hiss when the kids grab em by they tails an pull em round the yard. I don mind em none. I knows them gaters be too hot ta move fas enough ta get at my toes when I go up them porch stairs anyhow. We's got a Catahoula leopard dog I calls Gus, an he don even bark at them gaters when they crawls out the bayou an tries ta hide unda the porch. Gus an old dog now, he don mind them gaters neither. I sho would hate ta be a gater in July, though. People can get in front they fans, a dog can hang his tongue out he mouth, but them gaters just cook an cook inside they thick skins.

Now, I's been cleanin houses in Midnight since I done quit my schoolin ta help Mama when I's just out the tenth grade. My daddy he died in a car crash when I's but twelve year old an Mama needed help earnin money. She say the State of Mississippi weren interested in helpin folk who truly did need help so I had ta quit school an work at cleanin houses. I don think I missed much, ta tell the truth. Ruthie Mae, tha's my younger sister, she finished high school an she never left Midnight neither, an I done read ever book she brought home s I figure I's got ta be least as smart as somebody that done graduated from the high school. I's read me a play by Mistuh William Shakespeare, an a great book by Miss Harpa Lee – she from the South. We's got a cousin up St Louis way that went ta college, an he brought down a book a poems by a woman name of Maya Angelou oncet, an I sho did like some a them poems. 'Phenomenal Woman', yessa, I likes ta think that could be a poem bout me. Sometimes I reads that poem fore I goes ta sleep nights – I find it makes the thought a gettin up a mite easier.

Anyway, I's been cleanin these houses fuh goin on fiteen years now, an Lord if that don make me almost thirty-two year old! Tha's two an a half years of scrubbin floors all through the months of July an August when it s hot out the tar on Highway Number Forty-Nine makes sticky old tar bubbles. Cain't get that off yo shoes, no, sir, no matter what you scrubs em wit!

Most days I don mind none. I like that old Mrs Montgomery has her a cassette player what runs on batries so's you can carry it wit ya all through the house. A few year ago she took ta checkin 'books on tape' out the library in Yazoo fuh me ta lissen ta whiles I clean. I already done lissened ta *The Grapes a Wrath, Great Espectations* an *The Count a Monte Crista*. Mrs Montgomery's an old church friend a Mama's, so I stopped chargin her like I oughta a long time ago – tell the truth, I probably clean her house now so's I can lissen ta them books.

Mrs Montgomery an her husband, Eggar, moved ta Midnight when I's bout three year old. Eggar Montgomery come from a real wealthy family down Louisiana way – well, I spose they awful rich for black folk anyway. I guess his people did somethin wi shippin since slave days. Mighty dangerous, ya ask me, black folk helpin sell they kin up river. Anyway he waited a long time, till he fully grey-headed fore he got married. Mrs Montgomery — her Christian name rightfully Beetris but not even Mama call her that — was bout twenty-four when they got married, an twenty-five when they moved ta Midnight an she got pregnan wi Bobby.

Poor Mrs Montgomery never had nothin but trouble wi Bobby. Whole reason Mama took ta cleanin house fuh her was 'cause she's s sick she got liable ta retch her guts out ever six minutes or so. Why she didn want a proper doctor at the birthin, I'll prolly never know — but Mama went, s I went too. It ain't unusual fuh a woman round here ta have her baby at home, an usually they got four or five other women in the room with em. Nobody but Mama had chilen, s I just sat in the hall where Mama tole me ta stay an I waited. An lissened. Couple time I thought Mrs Montgomery musta died 'cause she yelled so mighty, an I hear Mama say, 'Now be the time ta pray, Sisters.'

An later Mama come out an tole me ta go tell Sister Maisha that Mr Henry be tryin ta steal the chile spirit fore the chile had a chance ta claim it for heself. While she had the door open tellin me zactly what ta say ta Sister Maisha, I looked past her white skirts into the birthin room. Mrs Montgomery was laid out on the bed wit a towel cross her forehead. Sister Jenkins an Sister Forres from the Baptist church was sittin on one side the bed, wearin long black skirts with they bibles open on they laps. Sister Bandele was standin on the other side the bed wearin white skirts like Mama, rockin back an forth, hummin – she had feathers in her hands an candles burnin on the winda sill. There was somethin drawn on the floor at her bare feet, an Mama had chalk dust on her hands, but I don remember what was drawed. Mama aksed Sister Jenkins ta read from the Gospel cordin ta John, an then she shut the door so's I couldn see any more.

S I ran out the Montgomerys' back porch an cross they lawn an down the dirt alley a spell ta Sister Maisha house. I started ta callin out 'Sister Maisha! Sister Maisha!' soon's I hit her front gate, an she come out the house s fast was like she been spectin me. She had blood on her dress, an when I aksed if she was all right, she say, 'Yes, chile, I be fine. What did yo mama say?' So I tole her an she flinch like I done hit her. She walk me back down the alley a spell into her backyard an she tole me ta tell the womenfolk under the door that she's goin take care of it – an she grabbed a dove from the coop an went back inside. Now, I know I's only four by the time Bobby got born, but I knew she an the rest a them ladies from Mama's other church was goin kill that dove. All 'cause a Mr Henry – but course I didn know nothin bout him then. Bobby did manage ta get born finally. Ash white he was when they let me see him first, but he turn beautiful Hershey-bar brown in a week's time.

Bobby was two, an I's almos seven year old when Ruthie Mae was born. We three spent mos our childhood together – me watchin out fuh them two mosly. I's always the mama in games, or big mama if they wanted ta play husban an wife. Ruthie Mae never knew our Big Mama 'cause she died when Ruthie was only a year or two old, but I likes to think I did a good impression a her fannin herself and speakin ta Mama in words I never could understand. I jus spoke gibberish, but Bobby and Ruthie Mae loved it.

Ventually I stopped watchin em, which I prolly ought not a done 'cause Ruthie Mae got pregnant when she's but sixteen year old. She was ficially goin out wit boy name a Fletcher Mandie, but we all knew who the daddy was. Ruthie Mae did tell Fletcher that she's goin marry Bobby an that she's sorry an all. But that Fletcher had him a wicked temper, an he said he's goin make sure Bobby an Ruthie never got married. Week an a half after that they found Bobby floatin face down in the bayou. I went ta identify the body – Mama sent me so's Mrs Montgomery didn have ta see her son that way. I wished I never had ta see a human body that way neither. Anyway, we all knowed it was Fletcher Mandie that done it – but he was sposedly in Atlanta wit his brother and cousin round when Bobby musta died so he never went to jail or nothin. Ruthie had the baby an named her Bella, after me – but shortly after that she started breakin mirrors, an screamin all the time. Mama say madness run in Daddy's side the family, so we put Ruthie in the hospital where she cain't hurt herself. But we all tell Bella who her daddy is, an she has a picture a him on her dresser.

S, like I's sayin, I left Mama an Bella bout five las Wednesday mornin ta try ta get ta Mrs Montgomery's house fore that tar started ta bubblin – a course Mrs Montgomery been at her sister's in New Orleans goin on two weeks now, but she don like no dust cumulatin in the house while she gone. S anyway, the stars was still out, I left s early! I member real clear lookin up an seein the stars in the shape a Mr Henry hat. That ain't never a good sign, 'cause Mr Henry be the spirit that moves souls from this world ta the next n. I hear tell down Lousiana way they call him by he proper name (*P★pa L★gba*) an they says it out loud. I think that be powerful bad luck though, s I's goin keep callin him Mr Henry – stay real respectful, see. Now, there wasn nobody else wandrin round town five in the mornin s I just looked down at the tar bubbles from the day afore where they raised an never did go down again.

S I let mself inta Mrs Montgomery's an started ta goin down the hall toward the cleanin closet when I saws it. Handprints in the dust on the mirror. Now, there ain't oughta had been dust in that house in the first place – not enough ta put handprints in anyway 'cause I done cleaned it five days fore that. S I decided I musta left a door unlocked, even though I done checked twice that ever door was locked fore I left it. I walked round an I checked em again an they's all still locked ceptin for the one I just come in at. S right away I calls the police 'cause I's worried bout Mrs Montgomery's jewels n things an I knows it's goin be my hide if anything be missin. I sit on the front porch, not lookin at the sky 'cause I's awful feared that Mr Henry's hat be up ta no good. When I were a little girl Mama use ta say Mr Henry hat only come out in the sky when spirits is movin. Wi the hat of stars out at night, I ain't shamed ta say that I's too scared ta stay in the house by mself.

S when the police car rolls up t the house it's Jeffy Bennett, an I tells him the story an we walks round the house again an he say he don know what ta think so he calls in somebody else. Just s happens that a Yankee boy what works with computers was up in Midnight from a police station in Jackson workin on Fletcher Mandie's murder las weeken. Now Jeffy wakes em up an brings em ta Mrs Montgomery's house an that Yankee boy keeps scratchin his eyes, sayin, 'What's wrong with this place? Hasn't anybody ever heard of sleep?' under his breath as he walks round.

He dusts fuh fingerprints, lifts he Mets baseball cap an scratches his eyes a lot, checks his portable computer an he makes a face like he's a-suckin on new lemons. Guess I weren posed ta be there still, but he aksed me nigh on ten times if them handprints hadn been there afore.

'Course they wasn, 'cause I's real good at my job,' I did say. An the Yankee boy looks at he computer n makes that lemon suckin face again an says, 'It says these fingerprints belong to a Robert C. Montgomery.'

Jeffy an I laugh an Jeffy say, 'They don teach you nothin at them Yankee schools, son. Bobby Montgomery died nigh on seven year ago!'

An that boy frowned again an turned he computer round fuh us all ta see how them handprints matched Bobby's prints from when he got rested fuh drivin under the influence a alcohol not long fore he died. It's real easy ta see how them little bumps an swirls match up perfect. An underneath it say his date a birth, then his date a death. After, it say how they found the body ('Suspected homicide – body found in bayou, in poor condition from bloat and animal damage'), an his ficial autopsy report ('Cause of death: collapsed trachea'), it say 'Case – Open'. Then we all make a face like we's suckin on lemons. Jeffy an I look t each other an nod some.

That Yankee boy he kept takin his Mets cap off an scratchin at his head like something was crawlin round on his scalp an he say, 'This simply doesn't make any sense.' An pushin buttons on that portable computer. He musta scanned them prints eight or nine times fore he just sat down on the front stair an shook his head like the answer might start printin out his ears like the computer print out a copy of Bobby arrest record if he wait long enough.

Jeffy goes n puts a hand on the boy shoulder, but the boy shakes he head an say, 'Look, the cleaning lady has to be mistaken.'

He shakes Jeffy hand off, an glares at me. 'Just admit that you've never cleaned the mirror. Fingerprints could last on something that's never been cleaned.' He frowns an looks at Jeffy. 'I mean, it's plausible that . . . it might be able to . . . I mean, under the right circumstances . . .' an his voice kinda fades out like car tail lights down the road.

Jeffy shakes he head an say, 'Now, if she say she done cleaned it then she did, son.'

That boy turn s red it almos cover the freckles on his nose.

'She can't have! These are definitely Robert Montgomery's prints, and if he's been dead that long she absolutely cannot have cleaned.' He waved his arms up an down with ever word.

Jeffy sighs, an looks at me. 'Stars awful bright out this mornin.'

An I nod n say, 'Some more'n others.'

An Jeffy shake his head an say, 'You seen some in the shape a hat?'

'Sho did,' I say an close my eyes.

Well, that Yankee boy sigh an say under he breath, 'This doesn't make any fucking sense.'

An Jeffy say, 'Listen, son, they's still a lady here.'

An he turn ta me an say, 'Sorry, Bella,' an we give each other a look that say cain't nothin be done bout them vulgar Yankees.

That Yankee boy stands up again an goes ta the mirror ta stand in front of Bobby's handprints, but he didn take he scanner wit him. He jus stood right in front them prints fuh musta been five minutes anyway. Finally he turn round an look t me an Jeffy an that white boy turned bout eight shades a green an he say, 'If you stand in front of those handprints, it looks like they're wrapped around your neck.'

An then, like he didn have no bones in he whole body, that Yankee boy fell in a heap. Jeffy barely manage ta catch his head fore it hit the floor.

Jeffy look up at me, from where he crouch down cradlin that Yankee like a giant white-green baby, an say, 'It sho ain't nothin we can control now. But it cain't hurt ta pour some sugar on a plate n stick a couple feathers in it by yo back door. You might oughta do that fore you leaves here.'

Course after all that, I jus wanted ta get home. I poured the sugar an found a feather ta put on it an I marched me back home, past them tar bubbles an didn once look up t them stars. I say ta mself, Mr Henry can keep his hat in the sky where it belong.

When I got home, the sun was jus startin ta peek through the cloud, makin the whole sky bright red. Bella was sittin on the porch, pattin Gus an hummin one a Mama's songs – a song bout spirits, but not from no hymnal. I sit down on the top step, an she come an sit on my knee. I hug her real tight, pat her head an say, 'Little Bella, you oughta be in bed still.'

An she lean her bony body inta my chest, an trace my collabone wit her tiny fingers an say to me, 'I couldn sleep no more, Auntie Bella. Gus started ta whinin, an you's gone already, an when I come out ta see if he OK, daddy was by the mailbox.'

I sighed somethin mighty an sent Bella back ta bed. I patted Gus while the sun come out an when I could start feelin the heat roll off the highway I went ta the shed ta find Mama's chalk. Be a long string a nights fore them stars move out the sky.

INDECISION

JOHN MC GEOWN

The lift is glass, and it rises swiftly, leaving the low-rise land-scape behind me. There are a hundred cities like this in Germany. They're not even cities, just giant identikit towns high on unemployment and low on culture. Weighed down by their own sense of history, where everything and nothing is a landmark to some past triumph. Where everyone knows their place, and yours.

The people below quickly shrink into pinpricks and the vehicles to toy trucks. If I reach my hand out I can pretend to pick men up and put them in front of the trucks. The girl beside me gives me a strange look, and asks what I'm doing.

'Playing,' I say.

'You're so stupid sometimes,' she says in her Continental accent.

That's part of me. I wasn't serious when I first met you either. We reach the top quickly.

'Tenth floor,' a voice says in German.

I take one last look out at the street below and go into the restaurant. The room is large, open plan, and we enter from the left of it. Straight away there is a bar beside us that runs the length of the wall until it hits a door that leads on to the balcony. The top of the bar is fake mahogany, to match the floor, and behind it there's an equally fake barman. He acts like an arsehole when I order drinks and we go to sit down.

'He thought you were a Brit,' she says. 'They still have a military base here.'

She's lived here all her life.

'I kind of am,' I reply.

There seem to be hundreds of tables in this restaurant, maybe because it's empty, or maybe because dusk is coming and they're all reflected in the windows. Every one is covered in a perfectly white tablecloth, and every tablecloth reaches perfectly halfway down the tables, exposing their Ikea legs. Wine glasses are perched downward and the cutlery gleams. There are only two other people in the place, another couple. We look at them and they gaze back, as if to say, *We know*.

I've got nothing in common with you, I think back. The waitress comes over and we order, then I tell her we're just going outside to the balcony for a bit, but we'll come back here to eat. She seems to understand. We take our drinks and as we walk past the bar to the door I feel the barman staring at me.

Outside, the balcony is wide and runs the whole length of the wall behind the bar. Wicker tables hug the wall with the same white tablecloths covering them, blankly this time. No dining al fresco here. I walk over to the edge and lean on the railing. I don't look down this time, just gaze at the sun setting over the roofs of the department stores and office blocks. It's nicer than inside. But there's nothing more to distract myself with.

She's standing beside me now. I've been forming the words in my head all weekend, but when I look at her they stick in my throat. You can't stay away from clichés sometimes; they're always based on the truth.

She looks at me expectantly. God, she has no idea it's coming. Her dark brown hair is half falling over her face, and the dying sunlight is glinting off it. Her blue eyes are wide. She seems so happy. Such a broad smile on such a perfect, thin face: so beautiful. I must be crazy to give this up.

Get back to reality. This isn't what you want. It's smothering you. She doesn't let you breathe. You're not happy. Beauty isn't everything. Christ! More clichés! Be honest with yourself. I am being honest.

The waitress is calling us. You've got to be kidding. We've only just come out here. Do they have the food ready-made in this country? Fucking German efficiency.

'Come on.' She smiles, then kisses me and leads me back into the restaurant. I know where I'm fucking going. I'm not a child. She sees the look on my face and laughs. She delights in this, loves getting the upper hand.

I'm sick of it, the back and forth, the constant battle for dominance. It never proves anything.

We share the starter in silence. Maybe we're all like that when we love for the first time. So powerless we try to dominate and control, so out of our depth we all obsess and manipulate. Do whatever we can to cling to the person we end up driving away. Love and hate aren't opposites; it's love and fear.

'Are you OK, baby?'

'Yeah, I'm fine,' I answer. 'Just hungry, that's all.' I kiss her on the cheek.

Coward.

'I love you *so much*.'

That's our thing. To add emphasis, or overcome the language barrier maybe. Not just I love you, but love you so much, love you to pieces, love you lots, love you to death. I used to think that the more I said it the more likely it was to come true.

'Love you too.' We rub noses.

Liar.

What happens is the more you say it, the more of a lie it becomes. But it's such a big lie it becomes reality, and you're the only one who sees the truth.

The main courses arrive and I order another drink. The first one has kicked in, heightened by my empty stomach. A few more and I won't think this way. A few more and all I'll see is her body, not her face. A few more and I'll bullshit my way through the rest of the night, the rest of the weekend, and say nothing.

It makes sense to say nothing anyway. After I leave we won't see each other for a few weeks, and I can do it by phone. It'd be easier on her that way. Easier on me, I won't have to see her heart break.

We share our dinners, picking at each other's food, feeding each other from our own. The barman and the other couple vacantly stare in our direction. This isn't done here, I suppose. But she likes to make a scene, likes to be looked at. I don't care. It's ironic, she's more affectionate in public than private. Only eager to demonstrate her love when people are watching. But I like it. Like being shown off, like being flattered, like a hypocrite.

I push the plate away and sit back. She's already finished.

'Let's get out of here,' I say, and call for the bill. I won't do it here. Won't do it today. Another drink and I'll forget all about it. I'm forgetting already. I glance down at her crossed legs underneath the knee-length skirt. The waitress interrupts with the receipt. We don't bother to tip.

On the way past the bar I give the barman a big wave.

'See ya, man!' I say loudly. He doesn't react. Fuck him.

The lift is still on this floor since we took it up. The party never stops here. As the doors close I push her up against the glass and kiss her. I slip my hand up her skirt, between her legs. She starts moaning. The lift hits the ground in no time. A few passers-by stare and I get embarrassed.

'Why did you stop?' she asks me.

'Are you serious?' I say. We walk into the street and I slide my hand into hers, so she can feel the moisture on my fingers. The air feels sharp, feels like I should be remembering something, but I've forgotten. She looks at me and smiles.

'There's a cool bar up ahead,' she tells me.

'Sounds good,' I say.

The Hot-Air Balloon

Andrea McNicoll

Mother Nong was crouched at the door of her kitchen, pounding garlic, ginger, chillies and shallots in a huge stone mortar to put in a curry for evening dinner, when she noticed a small hot-air balloon floating above the village, drifting slowly across the tops of the great banyan in the temple grounds. The festival of Loy Krathong was to start the next day, and more than a dozen hot-air balloons, which the villagers had made themselves, were strewn across the temple grounds, ready for the celebrations. A prize would be awarded by the district officer for the most gaily decorated one. They were to be fired up and set adrift the following night, symbolically carrying the villagers' sins as far away from the earth as mere human endeavour would allow. But it was most inauspicious to set the balloons adrift early and Mother Nong couldn't think who would have done it. The balloon appeared to have some small object attached to its string, but it was too far away to guess what the object might be. It probably had something to do with Mother Suree's boys, she decided, they were always up to some prank or other these days. Mother Nong felt sorry for Mother Suree, but lately she had begun to run out of patience, had even started to turn the other way when she saw her passing in the market. She glanced at the clock and started to pestle a little harder. Sergeant Yud would soon be home from the police station and he was always hungry. Few things pleased Mother Nong more than watching her husband tuck into his food, and the size of his belly, she felt, was evidence of her success as a wife. Why, only last week he had asked her to sew new panels into the trousers of his uniform. She stood up and lit the gas stove, pouring oil from a large tin can into a wok. She transferred the mortar's contents into the wok, added diced pork and chopped spinach, stirring and tossing the mixture with the spatula in her right hand as her left splashed in a liberal helping of oyster sauce. The lid of the pot in the electric rice cooker was trembling and steaming. Almost done, she thought with satisfaction, and time for a shower before he gets in. She turned off the gas and went into the bathroom. She had been to the hairdresser's that day, so she covered her head in a plastic cap to keep it dry. She slipped out of her sarong and scooped cold water from a huge earthenware dragon pot, throwing the water over herself, soaping and scrubbing vigorously. Rather than use a towel, she wrapped the sarong back around her wet body to prolong the sensation of cool so elusive during the daytime, and went upstairs to sit at her dressing-table mirror. Taking off the shower cap, she combed her hair. Nothing to be ashamed of, she thought, gazing at her reflection. She hadn't let herself go like Mother Suree. In the beginning, when her friend had confided to her one day over a bowl of noodles, Mother Nong had pointed out that a husband will stray only when his wife stops making an effort to look nice for him. She had taken Mother

Suree to the hairdresser's and they had even gone together on a shopping trip to buy some new clothes but her efforts had been in vain. Within a few days Mother Suree was back in her usual drab outfits, with her hair swept carelessly up into a bun at the back of her head. Really, the woman had no idea, thought Mother Nong, smoothing cream on her face and neck. Mother Suree had defended herself by saying she had no time to spend on her appearance, what with working all day in her green papaya salad stall. What was the point, Mother Suree had said, in dressing up in nice clothes when she had to cover them up with a big apron to stop the lime juice and fish sauce splashing all over them as she mixed the salads for her customers?

Mother Nong dressed and went back downstairs. It was six o'clock. She could hear the national anthem playing from the loudspeaker in the police station. Sergeant Yud would be lined up with the other officers on the clipped lawn in front of the station, saluting to the flag. He was a good man, she reflected. They had been married for twenty-five years already and had two grown-up children. Her daughter worked in the city as a secretary and her son had entered the monkhood at the beginning of Lent. She glanced at his picture on the wall, dressed in his saffron robes. The day of his ordination had been one of the proudest moments in her life. Mother Nong lit a candle and three sticks of incense and knelt down in front of the household shrine, repeating the words of an obscure Sanskrit prayer. The fact that she had no idea what it meant did not worry her in the slightest; she knew that by repeating it once every morning and once every night she would guarantee her family's continuing prosperity. She had bought the prayer for a small fee from the local fortune-teller who lived in a cave in the nearby forest and was famous for the accuracy of his predictions and the efficacy of his cures. He had arrived in the village too many years ago to count, having walked barefoot across the border from the Shan State in Burma, smoking a foreign-looking pipe, with nothing more than a cotton bag over his shoulder. It was rumoured he had been an important general in the Shan State Army, had fought alongside Aung San's Burmese soldiers in the war for independence against the British. He shared his cave with ridiculously large spiders, kept at bay by a posse of stray cats that the less tolerant villagers had chased away. He had prayers to answer every condition. He wrote them down from his prodigious memory on pieces of lined school paper and sealed them up in plain white envelopes. Mother Nong had taken Mother Suree to see the fortune-teller when she realised something more than a visit to the hairdresser was called for. The fortune-teller had asked Mother Suree the day and time of her birth and had set out the numbers in a triangle, which he surrounded with other numbers corresponding to the positions of the planets at her birth, counting furiously around the numbers with the tip of his astrologer's pencil.

'Five, six, seven, eight, nine . . . ah, yes. Well, this is not an auspicious year for you in matters of the heart. You should be very careful, you know, until the middle of next year when the position of Jupiter will change.'

'Is there nothing I can do?' Mother Suree had asked.

'The reason your husband is seeing another woman,' he had said, smoothing back his white hair and sifting through his pile of envelopes, 'is because you stole someone else's husband in your previous life. It's very simple really. I can give you a prayer to repeat every night and every morning and that will probably help but it's also a good idea for you to make some merit. According to your horoscope, your fund of merit at the moment is dangerously low. You really should have done something about this sooner. You should make a special offering as quickly as possible to the monks at the temple and buy seven catfish to set free in the temple pond.'

So the two women had gone together to the market to buy the seven live catfish kicking hopelessly around in a tub of water, and gifts for the monks. Mother Suree had taken all the money she had saved that month from her green papaya salad stall and had spent it on new robes and towels, instant coffee, tobacco and toothpaste, incense, candles, and tins of condensed milk and sardines in tomato sauce, which the two women had packed into baskets. On the morning of the next day Mother Nong had gone to collect her neighbour and had been pleased to see that Mother Suree had at least made an effort with her clothes and hair. Mother Nong had put on her third-best sarong for the occasion, made of a dark blue silk with delicate gold threads running through it. But Mother Suree hadn't even complimented her on her choice of sarong.

'He didn't come home again last night, Nong! I couldn't sleep a wink, waiting for the sound of his bike, his footsteps outside the door.'

'That's not so bad, is it? Why, even Sergeant Yud doesn't come home *every* night. But men are like that. It doesn't mean anything, Suree.'

'But do you know where Sergeant Yud is when he stays out all night? Does he tell you where he has spent the night?'

'Oh, I don't care to ask.' Mother Nong had smoothed out an imaginary crease from her sarong. 'Men don't like a woman who pries and nags, and asks too many questions. Besides, he's a policeman and sometimes he has to, well, take care of things. Things I might not understand.'

'But don't you worry he might be with another woman? In the brothel or the karaoke bar?'

'Of course he doesn't go to the brothel! I know he goes to the karaoke bar sometimes but only because the chief invites him – he can't turn down his boss now, can he?'

'But what's the difference? The karaoke bar is full of girls! Those young girls dressed up in miniskirts and high-heeled boots! Singing and dancing and goodness only knows what else! And you know what men are like when they have had a drink!'

'Exactly, Suree. If anything was to happen – and I'm not suggesting that it does – then it would be because of the alcohol and nothing more. Or because those girls are asking for it. Anyway, at our age we should be glad to be relieved of . . . well . . . our responsibilities, if you know what I mean. It's been a long time now since I've been interested in such . . . such *capers*. I can't help thinking that if Sergeant Yud spends a few nights somewhere else every so often then it's in my best interests!'

Mother Suree had been quiet then and the two women had walked through the village to the temple. To be honest, Mother Nong had been glad of an excuse to visit the temple, hoping to catch sight of her son. She had spotted him sitting cross-legged in the great hall, his shaven head bowed, his thin shoulder blades protruding from his robes, chanting sacred verses along with the other novices. It was such a relief to Mother Nong to know her son was safe. In the months running up to his ordination he had fallen in with a group of wild boys who drove too fast around the village on noisy mopeds, smoking and drinking and playing loud music. He had asked her constantly for money – too scared to ask his father – and it had been hard to refuse him, she loved him so much. She'd preferred not to think about what he might be spending the money on. Anyway, all that was over now. Nothing bad could happen to him whilst he was in the temple and it had made her so proud to see him in his robes. It was the greatest compliment a son could ever pay his mother and he had brought such merit to the whole family.

'Do you feel better now?' Mother Nong had asked as the two women walked back from the temple with empty baskets, the seven lucky catfish swimming happily around the temple pond.

'I suppose so.'

'And what about your prayer, Suree? Are you repeating it twice a day?'

'Yes, I'm doing all that.'

'Well, if all this doesn't work then nothing will!' Mother Nong had linked arms with her neighbour then, feeling she really had done her best to lend a helping hand. And there was merit in that too, after all.

Mother Nong spread a mat down on the floor and arranged the plates and cutlery on top. She would have enjoyed some green papaya salad as a garnish to the main dish but it was best these days to give Mother Suree as wide a berth as possible. It's not as though they had ever been that close anyway – not really. She had heard a rumour that Suree's husband was spending all his money on his minor wife now. Someone in the market had told her last week that Mother Suree had sold her gold necklace to help make ends meet. Apparently, she had even been seen one day shouting at the minor wife in the middle of the street. Such a loss of face! Suree would never live that down. A joke was going round the village that her papaya salad was the sourest in all Thailand, no matter how much cane sugar she put in. Mother Nong couldn't help smiling at that. She went into the kitchen and looked outside to see if her husband was on his way. Maybe he had to work late, she thought. No sign of him coming along the road yet but there was something unusual going on in the village. She went out into the road and peered along it. Men and women were leaning eagerly over their garden fences and at the end of the road, outside Mother Suree's house, a knot of people chattered and gesticulated. Those boys again, she thought, I bet it's to do with that hot-air balloon! Mother Nong shaded her eyes against the yellow sunset and took a few steps in the direction of the hullabaloo. She drew in her breath. Why, wasn't that Mother Suree being pulled out of her house by a policeman? What on earth had she done now? Mother Nong gathered up the ends of her sarong and ran along the road to join the crowd. Sure enough, there was Mother Suree, laughing like a madwoman, her hair undone, the white apron she wore at her stall all day hanging from her neck, covered in stains. Mother Nong spotted Sergeant Yud in the middle of the throng and pushed her way through to pull at his arm.

'What's going on?'

'You'll never guess what's happened! I can't believe a woman could be so . . . so . . . heartless!'

'What is it? Is someone dead?'

'As good as! That Suree woman – that so-called *friend* of yours . . .' Sergeant Yud shivered. 'It's too horrible! How could anyone do such a thing?' He flung his arms before him. 'The doctors can't help him now!' he warned.

Mother Nong tugged at her husband's arm. 'What do you mean? What has she done?'

'She only went and drugged her husband, then cut off his penis while he was sleeping! Cut it right off with the same knife she uses on her limes!' Yud paused, trying to absorb the horror. He struck his fist into the palm of his hand. 'I swear I'll never eat green papaya salad again!' He turned to his wife, staring at her fearfully. 'How could a woman do such a thing?'

Mother Nong clutched at her throat. 'But surely he can be taken to hospital and . . . and . . . have . . . it . . . sewn back on?'

'Oh no, she's too calculating for that! After she cut it off she tied it to a hot-air balloon and now it's floating away somewhere over the valley!' He pushed his wife to one side.

'There's no way I can face my dinner now! I have to go back and join in the search!'

And with that Sergeant Yud started up his moped and drove off, leaving Mother Nong open-mouthed in the middle of the road, watching the trail of trucks and bikes and dogs and children chasing a tiny gaily coloured dot that had drifted across the village on the back of the gentle evening breeze, and was slowly heading into a golden sunset above the rice fields.

GEORGE ANDERSON

Gannets!

One sparkling ice-blue day the gannets of the Bass Rock flew into the middle of Edinburgh looking for a certain politician.

The birds speak to each other. Pointing the beak skywards tells the mate: 'I'm off. Mind the egg.'

Beak-fencing says, 'You are my mate.' It looks to us like they are fighting, but for them it's like a kiss. They pair for life, and can live twenty-five years so they learn a thing or two along the way. They learned a thing or two about the politician.

Bin-raking gulls were the sea's spies in the city. The gulls told the eider ducks by the shore. The eiders told the puffins and the guillemots and the emerald-eyed shags on the May. Some gannets passing on their way to the Wee Bankie for sand eel, heard the gossip on the wind and came back to spew the news, along with the fishy sludge they fed their young.

The adults raised a whole generation of chicks with word of the politician. It was always whisky distilleries before geese. It was always ski tows before ptarmigan. And worst of all, it was always greedy-netted trawlers before seabirds.

The young gannets sidled uneasy in their nests between feeds, and eyed each other across the gleaming white guano which spattered the Bass. For weeks they plumped and fluffed, then come the time hurled themselves off the rock to splash down gracelessly in the North Sea.

Then they started swimming to Africa. They were bigger than their parents, and too heavy to fly yet. They broke the monotony of the voyage by plotting. Paddling shrank them until they were fit for the air. Most of them took off from the English Channel, and then headed across the Bay of Biscay, past Spain and on to the African coast. There they fed and debated for two whole years, sharpening their skills, before returning back north to the rock.

At this point the young birds would normally have spent a couple of years going through the motions of breeding – courting and nesting but failing to lay. Just practising. But this generation had other plans. Plans honed on the wing off Senegal and Morocco, Sahara grit in their turquoise eyes.

They could go as far as Norway on feeding trips, so it was easy to visit the parliament. Ten thousand of them streamed up the Forth, ducking under the rail bridge and fanning out over the road bridge. They came together in a big white dart again, their lemony heads straining forwards. People looked at them in amazement as they headed over the city, and they caused the One o'Clock Gun to go off at two minutes past.

The politician was outside the parliament being interviewed by a TV crew when people began pointing. When he followed everyone's line of sight and saw the gannets approaching, he somehow knew they had come for him. His feet were fixed. He didn't raise his arms.

Gannets feed by making their peace with gravity. Flight has taken millions of years of evolution but a gannet will turn its back on this heritage, fold up its hard-won wings and plunge into the sea at seventy miles an hour. So their skulls are like crash helmets, and they have airbags just like cars, that inflate on impact, behind their eyes, round their brain and throat.

But that didn't save the birds as they hurled themselves at the politician, smashing first on his head, then on his collapsed body, and finally on the piled corpses of their fellows. The birds poured out of the sky on to where the man had been. The TV crew got it all on tape. The nation saw it all that night. The politician was dead in seconds.

Dave's Devastatin' Art

Garthamlock Dave McConochie was the black sheep of his family. Every wan o thum was oan the make mind you. Dinna get me wrang there. Naw, but the thing wis that where the rest o them were intae obvious kindsa dodges, yer man Dave wuz mair imaginative.

He hud red in the paper that there were many sheckles to be made palming off all sorts of guff to the cognoscenti, as art and such – boys carvin up coos and lassies wi untidy rooms and that.

Never wan tae go by hauves, Garthamlock decided tae dae the thing right, and went tae coalidge. Efter awe, a wee bit posh totty fur a coupla years wisnae gonnae go amiss. Am ah right? An then payday would come in a coupla years, an if it didnae, well he's hud a bit posh.

So oanywye. Garthamlock Dave has a total terr for three years and he is the favourite o wan and all at the coalidge. Just the very boy for the lecturers lookin fur a bit o working-class authenticity, and by Goad wis he no jist the sodger as well for every Fiona looking furr a bit o ruff.

And then it came time for Davey's degree show, an his choice of expression was maistly influenced by a nippit wee bint he hud fallen in wi, who was intae green politics an that.

Hudd Davey oan a bike this wan. Him thit hud been dain up auld moaters since he wis fifteen year aul. She let him take the bus if it wus rainin mind. This wis a big relief tae Big D, despite the fact he hud always said busses wur fur refugees.

Nippit is it? Christ!

Oanywye, whit Davey pit thegither fur the degree show wis a piece o conceptual art outlining how to go about staging a complete attack on the transport system o central Scoatlin. It wis cried 'The Master Plan'.

If truth be told, he nailed a series of bits o pepper tae a big slab o wid, which wis papped up in the gallery fur the show. Oan each bit o pepper there was scrawled, in biro, sketch plans for various dodges tae bugger things up.

So wan involves six neds appropriatin a vehicle each an dain a wee bit formation flying oot there oan the M8. Jist past the Stepps bypass they wis tae coordinate intae a rolling, five-mile-an-hoor, strung-oot-across-the-lanes ned display team, playin euphoric trance music loud oan the stereos, wi aw the windaes wound doon. This wid cabbage the whole shootin match near back tae Greenock, although I believe the trance music wisnae whit ye wid cry essential.

Anither wan involved boays stoapin stolen corrs in the off-ramps o multi-storey car parks – jackin them up then shootin the craw wi aw the wheels.

An then there wis wan aboot six corrs doing laps of a roundabout at rush hour. Anither aboot folk dressed as Arabs wi backpacks at the airports, an wan aboot folk going on trains and jist shoutin: 'Zat a bomb?!' while pointing at sombdy's luggage.

It wint oan like that fur page efter page, wellied up oan this big bit o wid. And oan the biggest piece of paper wis neatly typed – nae biroed by the way, but neatly typed – the suggestion that if all of these measures should be enacted at the yince, then an entertainin spectacle wid ensue, fur those of a dissenting and ecological disposition.

Noo, Davey's coalidge wisnae that highly regardit, so the degree show didnae attract awe that much attention. Who-an-ever, wan critic fae a posh clever paper turned oot fur a shuftee, goat a keek at 'The Master Plan', and thocht tae himsel: 'Ah could get a bit mileage oot o this.'

These boays are aw the same, mark you, so the wan at the posh clever paper goat onty his mates at a posh stupit paper, and from there it was a short whisper tae the rough stupit papers.

Whichever way ye want tae paint it – Garthamlock's degree show dodge wiz aw owwer the news-stands the next day. And by Christ wis there no outrage!

How dare this hairy wee shite go popagatin this dangerous nonsense? Hairy-arsed bloody New-Aged protest oan the rates, screamed the blatts.

Noo of course, ordinarily, a few hunner middle-class posers would have chuckled at McConochie's creation an scratched their chins an nodded knowingly afore jukin awa fur a wee pop at the Chardonnay. Nae herm wid be done. Bit naw. The papers, in order tae fully illustrate the horror of whit had been perpetrated in the name o art, hud tae print the hail bloody thing.

Well ah'm here tae tell you, it was a bluidy disaster aw roon.

Did a band o activists no take up Davey's scribbling tae hert, and go oot an enact aw that stuff he hud biroed! Wan Friday efternoon they took oot the M8, the Erskine Bridge, the Forth Road Bridge, car parks, trains, planes an even the odd ferry. Christ, they even made up the bridge bits themselves, stoapin three corrs haufwye oot, then going back the line o traffic wi screwdrivers, chibbing aw the tyres. That bit wisnae even in 'The Master Plan'. Call it their ain flourish, if you will.

Let me tell youse, there was a fair bit o inconvenience tae the travlin public. And by Goad, the constabulary failed tae see the funny side. They reckoned fower fowk died because o ambulances nae getting through. Pizzas wurny delivered – that sort of stuff. It wis the talk o the parliament, the papers, the TV and radio, bars, everywhere, everybody hud an opinion oan it.

Wan discussion programme oan the wireless posed the question: could all this chaos be blamed oan Davey's art?

Furthermore, wis art too dangerous to be allowed tae go swedgin aroon in real life like that? Should it nae be kept safe in galleries an such where it widnae bother anybdy?

'Could the laddie no jist paint something?' said wan caller, voicing the opinion of many like her.

Noo the newspapers stertit condemning the art, but then the radio pointed oot that it wis the newspapers thit allowed the daft wee bits o hairy kids tae read the thing. The radio, by the way, wis maist pit oot that they hud missed the story in the first place.

So the question wis, wis it ideas that needit tae be banned, or jist art? Or wis it stupidity that needed tae be banned? A few fowk even said it should be corrs that wir banned, bit naebody took oany notice o them.

The papers hud one last tilt at the thing oan the back o this, an then moved on tae some other guff.

Bit Garthamlock Davey McConochie learned his lesson and he gave the conceptual a bodyswerve thereafter.

KIRSTEN ANDERSON

Dad in the Drawer

Mum hopes Dad died just before her alarm went off. Otherwise she'd been lying next to a dead body for hours. She got into bed after him that night, after late-night *Trisha* was finished, and sometimes she looks puzzled and starts to say, 'Was he cold? Was he cold?' I wait for her to say more, but she never does. She just leaves the question hovering there between us. I don't think she likes the idea of getting into bed with a dead body *and* sleeping next to it all night long.

When she screamed I jumped out of bed so fast that I didn't remember to put on my Tinkerbell slippers. I realised as soon as I stepped outside my bedroom. I hate the feeling of my bare feet on the wooden floors that Mum insisted we had put down last year. She said she wanted the whole house to look like a Scandinavian lodge and pretended to have come up with the idea by herself. I know she stole it straight from a magazine though. Because she announced her big interior design plans after seeing some pictures of a woman from *Coronation Street* who'd just had her lips done and was celebrating her new look by inviting readers inside her beautiful home, which 'inspired by her love of all things

Swedish and minimalist'. I remember because I looked up the word 'minimalist' in my *Oxford English Dictionary*. It pays to enrich your word power. I read that in one of my grandpa's copies of *Reader's Digest* and think that it's very good advice.

I'm not a minimalist. Especially not now. My room is the only one in the house with a carpet but you can hardly see it as it's covered with toys and books and DVDs. I feel safe with all these things around me. And I never have cold feet like I did when I stood at Mum and Dad's bedroom door that morning.

Cold feet = Dad's blue face + bulging eyes + mouth hanging open.

If you ask me, he was definitely dead long before the alarm went off otherwise he'd have looked beautiful and peaceful like they do in the films. I don't mention this to Mum though. She'll just tell her new boyfriend Tommy and he'll get mad. He has to sleep in that bed now you know.

Most of the time I stay here in my room and watch *The Sound of Music*. It's research. I want to be a nun when I'm old enough and I practise every night. My granny gave me a cross necklace. Solid pewter, she said. It weighs a ton and hurts my neck a bit but a nun's life is all about suffering so I better get used to it I suppose. I wear a towel on my head, kneel by my bed and talk to God. People think that religion causes nothing but wars and pain and suffering but it doesn't. It's people that ruin everything. If I was God I'd be really upset. After all the trouble he went to creating us and then sending his own son to die for us too. People forget about everything he's done, but they'll be sorry. That's what Father Patrick says.

When Mum was only sixteen she got pregnant and a lot of people thought she should get rid of it. But not Father Patrick. He sat her down and gently gave her the facts in what Mum calls his Val Doonican voice – he said if she were to go ahead and follow the others' advice that would make her a murderer and her little baby (that was me!) would be screaming and wriggling about in agony inside her womb as it was sucked out, bit by bit. She didn't like the sound of that so Father Patrick kindly pulled some strings so she and Dad could get married and everything turned out fine in the end. So I suppose I have a lot to thank him for too.

I feel a bit guilty sometimes because if Mum had decided to get me sucked out, she may have been a murderer but she also could have been a beauty therapist and nail technician. That's what she was going to do at college. She sometimes gets sad about the fact that she was forced into a loveless marriage and made to abandon her dreams but she says that it was God's will and I know what she means. It's just like when Maria was forced to leave the abbey to be a governess for the von Trapp children.

Dad didn't like all the God talk. He said it was a load of shite and that there was no God, no Jesus, no Mary and definitely no heaven. Once you're dead you're dead, he said. He used to have a long lie on Sunday mornings when we went to Mass and he didn't come to my first Holy Communion, which is a shame because I looked beautiful in my white dress. Ethereal, Father Patrick said. According to my dictionary, that could mean that I looked eerie or otherworldly or maybe delicate, which in turn can mean insubstantial. I worried about this for a while but Father Patrick was smiling when he said it, so I've taken it as a compliment.

I hadn't wanted to make Dad angry by dressing up like a *fucking bride of Christ* but I really, really wanted that dress and I knew the lace veil that came with it would come in handy when I wanted to do my nun thing. It's wrapped in white tissue paper in a box under Mum's bed and it's hard to sneak it out without her or Tommy noticing, which is why I make do with a towel most nights.

Mum says Dad was very lucky that Father Patrick agreed to do the funeral at St Benedict's after all the terrible things he had said about the Catholic Church over the years. Especially the stuff about kiddie-fiddlers. If it had been up to Dad, he would have had his body chucked on a skip like a piece of rubbish, but instead we had him cremated as a compromise, which caused a bit of a stir. Mum says burials are really the way to go in the Catholic Church. She put Dad's ashes in a copper box thing and sat it on the bedside shelf next to her Jackie Collins collection, but Tommy took it down when he moved in and put it in the kitchen drawer. He said it was giving him the freaks.

I take it out of the drawer and bring it in here every night when I do my nun practice. It makes me feel like Dad's with me. Apparently he's with me all the time but the thing is, I know Dad and when he woke up in heaven and realised that we were all right about the afterlife thing, he'd have been raging. So it's best that I chat to him in private so he doesn't feel stupid. I'm hoping that one night soon he might appear to me in a vision like Gabriel did to Mary.

I'll have to be patient with him though, so I never pray over the copper box for too long. When I'm finished, I put on my Tinkerbell slippers and tiptoe through to the kitchen and put Dad back in the drawer.

The Man (excerpt)

'Things were so good in the beginning.'

How often have you heard that line? Or said it yourself? People say it all the time and when they do you can be pretty sure their present situation isn't looking too hot. It takes a while for things to get so bad that you start searching your memory for a time when they weren't. Looking for some sign you missed that led you to today. When the fact of the matter is things probably weren't that great back in the beginning either. Think about it. In years to come, you're going to talk about the life you're living now and you'll probably do it with a whimsical sigh, all misty-eyed. *Those were the good old days.* That's what you'll say. And are you really that happy just now? Probably not. But you can rest assured you'll look back one day and rewrite history. But how can you be blamed for that? How can any of us be? It's how we get through life. Especially when it comes to love. We all have selective memories about love. David is no exception.

Just ask him and he'll tell you all about how good it was in the beginning. Love's young dream. That's what he and Abigail were apparently. David had read somewhere that when it comes to looks in a relationship, like attracts like. He wasn't convinced about this theory until he got together with Abigail, his first proper girlfriend. Then he realised it must be true. If he'd been forced to choose he would have said that he was the more attractive of the two, but there was no denying what a good-looking couple they were. Abigail wasn't the kind of girl he thought he'd end up with and he knew his mother would have preferred him to settle down with a nice quiet girl from university but he knew Abigail was the one. He also knew that his mother would have complained regardless of who he married as she was that kind of woman: only happy when she had reason not to be. He put that down to her Frenchness, something his father had told him all about just before he died. David was only eight years old at the time but he still remembers the conversation. Word for word. Because it was the last conversation they ever had.

'OK, son,' his father had wheezed. 'Pretty soon you're gonnae be the man of the house and you're gonnae have to know how to deal with your mother.'

David was sitting wide-eyed by the bed, desperate for the secret knowledge his father was about to bestow upon him.

'Your mother's kind – the frogs I mean – they're all the same. They're ay moanin' about somethin'. Dour-faced bastards, the lot o' them. So just let it go in one ear and oot the other. You'll be just fine if you remember that. OK, son?'

'OK, Dad,' said David, 'I'll remember.'

David sat for a minute or two, pondering over what he'd just been told. The only noise in the room was the sound of his father's chest rattling with each in-breath.

'Dad?'

'What, son?'

'If you don't like frogs, then why did you marry one?'

'Because your mother was a looker,' his father said with a raspy laugh and a wink. 'She still is. So I overlooked the French part.' He groaned as he used his elbows to manoeuvre his skeletal frame into an upright position. 'That's another thing I want you to remember, son. You have to make allowances for love. Never forget that.'

When David got to a certain age, he discarded a lot of the opinions his father had given him and stopped using the term *frogs*. But he knew there was no escaping the truth in his father's words. The French *were* all dour-faced and fifty years of Glasgow living had done nothing to improve his mother's demeanour. Nor had it affected her accent, which was thicker now than it had been when she arrived aged seventeen. Abigail used to say his mother laid it on thick in an attempt to sound exotic and interesting and that no one could live in Glasgow all that time and end up more French than they were in the first place. Out of loyalty, David told Abigail that his mother just had a very strong accent and that becoming a widow at such a young age had done strange things to her. Perhaps it was an identity thing, a cry for help, he'd said. He told her he'd read about these things and would rather she kept her stupid opinions to herself. But deep down, David knew Abigail was right. His mother sounded like someone from *'Allo 'Allo!* in public, but underneath she was as Glasgow as a deep-fried Mars bar.

I told you to ask David if you wanted to hear about the good old days with Abigail, but you wouldn't even need to ask as it's all he talks about now. It's part of his defence, I suppose. He's desperate to let people see that he's not a bad man. He appreciates that taken as an isolated event, what he did to Abigail does seem horrific. But he's worried that people won't take into account what a devoted husband he's been. That things hadn't always been bad. David had just been intent on recapturing that happiness he and Abigail had shared in the beginning and what he did was the last in a long line of attempts to make things good with her again. He says that he'd had no other choice. No choice whatsoever. Not if he wanted to make his marriage work. And that's all he's ever wanted. To be a happily married man like he was in the beginning. He doesn't think that's too much to ask for.

He'll tell you it was a whirlwind romance. That they never spent any time apart and never socialised with other people as they were in love to the point of obsession and didn't want anyone else's presence to dilute that love. Oh, and he'll definitely tell you about the first time Abigail saw him naked and how her jaw dropped at the size of his manhood. But that's men for you. What David won't tell you is that his and Abigail's wasn't the ideal marriage scenario, what with his being Catholic and her being six months pregnant and not Catholic. And the baby? Well, the fact that he had, on a few occasions, managed to keep his gargantuan penis hard long enough to penetrate Abigail for a few seconds allowed him the luxury of deluding himself that the baby was actually his.

Of course, on some level he knew he was fooling himself. And not just about the baby. There were question marks hanging over a lot of things but David chose to ignore them.

He needed Abigail. He loved her. And to David that's all that really mattered. Abigail wasn't very forthcoming with her feelings for him, but David blamed that on her poor communication skills, which he'd explained to Abigail she would have to improve if she wanted to accompany him to business events in the future. He would be happy to help her of course. He liked to think of himself as Henry Higgins to her Eliza Doolittle. Abigail was a little rough around the edges but David was confident he could handle that, along with the obvious problem of her low EQ.

David considers himself an expert on emotional intelligence, having read various books on the subject. Although it's quite a controversial opinion, he thinks a high EQ is much more important than a high IQ, and as someone who scores highly in both, he feels able to make that judgement, confident that he is right. So in David's opinion, it was a combination of Abigail's low EQ and lack of verbal skills that rendered her unable to express her feelings for him. Not to mention her low self-esteem. David reckoned she was suffering from that too. She had begun to eat for two as soon as she found out she was expecting, which David had told her was not necessary as he'd read that the pregnant body only needs a couple of hundred extra calories a day in the first trimester. But she didn't listen. And the bigger she got, the more she seemed to be down on herself and everyone around her, especially him. He had been worried about the implications of having a wife with a low EQ *and* low self-esteem. Not to mention a fat wife with a low EQ and low self-esteem, but then he remembered his father's words about having to make allowances for love. So he put these worries to the back of his mind and looked forward to the day this beautiful woman would be his wife. He was sure marriage would solve every problem they had. And he would prove all those doubters wrong. Especially his mother. Abigail wasn't with him for any reason other than love. True love. And he was so excited about that first dance with her. That's when it would all change. That's when it would all seem real, he'd told Abigail.

She hadn't said anything.

That first dance ended up haunting him for years and in the end it made him do what he did to Abigail. The stuff you'll have read about in the papers. Abigail had said on their wedding day that it had been a simple error on the DJ's part and that hardly anyone had even noticed. Not that it matters now. Simple error or act of sabotage, it didn't change the fact that their first dance, the dance he'd been longing for, wasn't to Al Green's 'Let's Stay Together', as had been agreed two months previously. Instead, in front of family and friends, their first dance as man and wife was to the Rolling Stones' 'Satisfaction (I Can't Get No)'. He remembers the beautiful Abigail, who'd successfully hidden her pregnancy under an explosion of white taffeta, laughing like a drain and gesturing to her friends who eventually joined her on the dance floor. This left David with no choice but to return to the top table and to his mother, who pulled him into his seat by his sleeve and muttered, 'It isn't too late. I warned you!' And in her much louder French voice reserved for occasions such as this, 'I cannot believe zat gold-digging leetle slut is vearing white.'

So that is the beginning David describes as 'so good'. He was kidding himself then and he's kidding himself now. And David is an intelligent man. Not that this matters I suppose, as even stupid people must know when they are kidding themselves. It's a feeling more than a fact. But love will do strange things to you. Make you hide the truth from yourself. And sometimes this is harmless. I mean, we all wear rose-tinted glasses from time to time, don't we? But David's niggling doubts were like dead bodies he'd thrown into a lake. And one by one they slowly rose to the surface, looking all the more ugly for having been down there for so long.

FIONA BINGHAM

Ignorance and Innocence

> Ring o' ring o' roses
> A pocket full of posies
> Atishoo! Atishoo!
> We all fall down.

Theresa was only seven and had already been singing about death for a couple of years now, except she didn't know that yet. Her mother stood with the other parents, watching, while the children finished their games before being dragged home. Marissa decided she would take Theresa to Eyam where she could learn what 'we all fall down' *really* means. There was a part of her that was loath to spoil a child's innocence but she would not have her child growing up ignorant, especially about death. Besides, it would be good for her to learn some local history; Theresa would learn enough about London's plague at school.

Marissa was impressed: Theresa had really enjoyed the trip. They had played in the village stocks, read all the plaques on the cottages where people had died and seen the place where they left money soaking in vinegar so the neighbouring village could get payment for provisions without risk of infection. The part Theresa had loved the best was hearing all the different cures people tried, like drinking fat.

'Yuk!' she'd said, pulling a face. 'People really did that?'

'Well, they didn't have the medicines we have now and they didn't want to die, so they would try anything,' Marissa had told her daughter.

The next day at school, Theresa couldn't wait to tell all her friends what the rhyme really meant. At first they didn't believe her, but a teacher overheard their conversation and confirmed it was true.

'But, Mrs Johnson, that's stupid! Why would people think flowers would make them better?' one girl said.

'Well, Suzie, we still give flowers to people who are ill, to cheer them up because flowers look and smell nice, so maybe it's not such a silly idea.'

They were going to do painting that afternoon and Theresa was already thinking about those pictures of people who had the plague she'd seen at Eyam. Purple and red were her favourite colours.

Marissa had taken Theresa to school and was preparing for a day in front of the computer, writing appraisals. She let her laptop power up while she made herself coffee, and then settled herself in front of the bay windows, looking out into the garden so she could enjoy one of the last days of wintry sun. Every time the light changed slightly with the movement of the clouds she would look up, as if something was watching her from the garden. There was nothing there, but the quiet of the house was gnawing at her stomach and she found her breathing was getting faster. Too much coffee? she wondered. She turned the computer off. Maybe she could get back to it this afternoon. She went up to the window and looked out. It was sunny but the frost still lay thick across the grass and the trees seemed to shiver in the wind. She decided she would go for a walk to clear her head, though she couldn't understand what was making her feel like this. She picked up her hat and gloves and wrapped her neck in the long soft scarf Ben had bought her last Christmas on his way back from Asia. She liked to think she could still smell the market spices and dust from the desert, but she had washed it too many times since then for that to be true, and all she could really smell was the faint lingering of the perfume she had on the last time she wore it. Marissa left the house, smiling to herself as she played with the tassels.

When she came back half an hour later, her cheeks and ears were pinched red with cold and her fingertips were numb within her gloves, but the smile was still there and her eyes had cleared. She stood leaning against the kitchen work surface, letting her mug of tea warm her hands. A key turned in the front door. She looked up; Ben must have come home early. He stood in the doorway, slightly stooped as he was too tall for it, and looked at her. She put her tea down and straightened. His whole face seemed frozen but his eyes were saying too much for her to process at once. He took a letter out of his pocket and placed it in her hands, stroking her shoulder gently before going upstairs.

No words. Nothing to say; they had done this so many times before but they had thought that the last time was the last. She looked at the letter in her hands; the envelope was still warm from his pocket. She knew what it would say, didn't want to see the cold, printed truth, but knew that soon that might be all she had. She sat down and hugged herself. Three months. She was suddenly very tired but had a great urge to get up and run. Three months; she kept still. It was so much better than when they had first married; they had hardly seen each other in those days. He would miss Christmas again. She could hear him moving about upstairs, packing, and tried to memorise every footstep. Three months and a third of the sounds of this house would be gone. She stood. His reluctant feet neared the bottom of the stairs. She couldn't help smiling, Ben always looked good in his uniform. Bags packed at his feet. She put her hands on his shoulders and let them find their way to his wrists where he caught them and held them. Three months without this face.

He gave her two envelopes – one for her, one for Theresa – and watched Marissa put them in the bottom kitchen drawer. He hated that he was watching her do this again, this little ritual they had perfected, that kept them breathing. He put his arm around her waist and pulled her towards him. They stood holding each other, breathing in their disappointment-dappled love. A horn sounded outside and still holding her hand he shouldered his bags. He opened the door and turned back to let his eyes remap her face and then kissed her forehead so tenderly that all her carefully woven strength suddenly unravelled.

'I love you.'

He was gone. She shut the door. She went to the kitchen to make some lunch; soon it would be time to pick up Theresa from school.

The Glass Coffin

After choking on a piece of poisoned apple, Snow White was laid in a glass coffin in the forest. The whole world could come and visit her deathbed but, according to Disney at least, it was only the animals and dwarfs that did. That is until the prince arrived. He seemed to be the only one who thought of trying to resuscitate her, and you would think an interest in kissing a dead stranger, beautiful or not, might make him a little suspect as a potential husband. But then it is a fairy tale and we are taught to suspend our disbelief.

Far, far away in the Middle Kingdom a man called Mao Ze Dong, a man known to all the people of the kingdom, died. Although not known for his great beauty, he too was placed in a glass coffin so that the people could see him. The man had made such a difference that long ago it seemed the people of the Middle Kingdom had tattooed the name of Mao across the heart of their nation like the name of a lover. There are a few, however, who murmur regretfully about this permanent needlework. The red ink has spread even to Xinjiang, the last outpost of the Middle Kingdom. It is so different from the capital and the eastern provinces and yet Beijing is capital here too. The people who live in this dry, dusty land are not Snow White's dwarfs but the Uighur. Although Mao's coffin lies in

Beijing, the Uighur are not alienated by distance, for in the centre of the provincial capital of Kashi is a Tian'anmen-style square and one of the largest statues of Mao in the country. Despite the fact that the sun cannot rise at the same time for both Beijing and Kashi, the Middle Kingdom only has one time. The presence of Mao Ze Dong cannot fade into myth merely through distance or death.

In Beijing he continues to smile benevolently over the entrance to the Forbidden City, and scattered throughout the twenty-seven provinces, miniatures of this moled face are reproduced and hung reverently in wilting homes. This Snow White (perhaps better called Rose Red) was laid to rest in a glass coffin in a glass room at the age of eighty-three but, despite the soldiers who guard him and the throngs of people who come to see him, there is no miracle. There is no resurrection; no Mulan has come to take the poison from Mao's throat. They called it the Cult of Mao: the unrestrained fervour that carried the people for so long through the Cultural Revolution. Now a temple has been built to house his mausoleum. Each pilgrim or curious traveller must leave their worldly possessions in the hands of the baggage attendants but is asked not to leave anything of value. Once visitors are reconciled to this riddle, and sufficient offerings have been purchased, the river of traffic separating Mao from his people must be crossed. There is no ferryman to take you across Beijing's Styx and long gone are the days when pedal power ruled the roads. Taking your life in your hands like a gift and finding safety in the numbers of those with you, you cross and find yourself awaiting approval from the guardians of the shrine entrance: the Beijing police. It does not matter that the metal detectors let you pass in silence; the guardians will still search you and every pocket bulge must be accounted for.

The queues are long and the children begin to get tired and bored. Parents appease the hawkers selling flowers and send their children off to buy some with a handful of crinkled paper carrying the dead man's face. The entrance hall is large and empty except for a great white marble statue of the man himself. The children are dwarfed by the smiling man, sitting fat and jolly like a Marxist Santa. They run to put the flowers at his feet, returning to parents a little shyer, perhaps a little more in awe. The queue keeps moving and pauses at a rope barrier where more men in uniform direct your path and there he is. Snow White's forest glen is replaced by a trapezium-shaped room with two armed centurions at the back wall and one door. You are encouraged to pay your respects quickly before continuing on your journey. This is not a place of final peace and rest, but quiet fear. The people of the Middle Kingdom who live for ever as ancestors are worshipped, and those who feel neglected return to remind the family of filial obligations. This once-imposing man was seen as a father, perhaps now a great ancestor who needs pacifying. The guards are there to discourage loiterers: both the zealous in worship and the zealous in anarchy are unpredictable. Their guns may not even be loaded, but few could get inside unnoticed. You are not even allowed to take water bottles, for fear of what it is uncertain – that we might throw them at the reinforced glass, which is probably bullet-proof?

The parts of the room that are not transparent are red and about the coffin stand the various flags of the nation and the party. It was Sun Yat Sen who founded the republic but it was Mao that made its land red and filled its sky with golden stars. Yet across his body is laid not the flag of his people but that to which he dedicated his life: the Hammer and Sickle. Mao Ze Dong, of great physical and political stature in his prime, now lays his shrunken form in a small open casket. His pillow allows light to be shone beneath his head, to minimise his deathly glow. Sadly the excessive orange hue only increases the body's likeness to Madame Tussaud's waxworks and the pilgrim is left wondering if they have been cheated out of their entrance fee. Would Mao's body really be put on display for all to see, or is this just a model and the real one is somewhere else, cryogenically frozen, perhaps?

It is quite normal for leaders and heroes, the beloved of a place, to lie in state for a day or two while people come from miles away to pay their respects and say goodbye. It seems strange, however, to keep someone in state for thirty years. The people who come are no longer mourners. They are a riot of races; their causes to fight left with their bags, though the majority are local to the Middle Kingdom. They are tourists, students, historians, voyeurs and worshippers. The man, who chose atheism to enlighten his people, is now enshrined in glass like Snow White in the fairy tale, in a temple of history. What would have happened if Snow White had never been wakened? Those who knew her would have been faithful to her graveside, until they too died, and then the forest would have claimed her as its own.

Noir et Blanc

Marie-Anne Mancio

It was red first. You courted me by bringing me slithers of red food, mostly tinned (tomatoes, peppers, chillies, strawberries, raspberries, cherries, redcurrants), then food you had dyed red. In our most passionate period, you dyed all food blue. Blue porridge, blue rice, blue bananas sliced on blue yoghurt, blue milk. We were young; we did not worry about E-numbers. I was your model once. I posed upright and mostly clothed, my legs cramping from standing still so long, and I watched you mix your colours expertly on a palette. I had noticed you on campus because you were better dressed than the other students. You were a broad, handsome man with thick black hair and eyes of swimming-pool blue. A group of us were drinking in a bar with a Moroccan theme. There was drapery and round, mosaic-topped tables: white billows over blue and gold.

'Tell me who you are,' you said, in your hybrid accent.

'Alice.'

The following morning there was a note in my mailbox:

Dear Alice,
In order to develop our relationship further, we should
enter a dark room and discuss our mutual exposure. Allow

me to focus on your apertures; perhaps to indulge in
roll play . . .
Do not reply in the negative.
Sebastian

I found your work space in the studio. Exuberant paint-ings: tiny monochrome figures floating across the surface of red ground. I typed a reply:

Dear Sebastian,
You paint a good portrait of yourself. I think you're a drip
for pouring out your heart to me, but I'm tempted by your
hard-edged distraction.
Alice

After six nights, I capitulated. I had dared you to run naked with me across the college lawn at midnight. We did it breathily, for no other reason than we ought not to. It was a bitter night, starless, and the wind whipped our limbs and ears and noses.

'You are crazy, Alice Glass,' you panted. 'Mad as the Mad Hatter.'

'Shouldn't that be the March Hare?'

You overtook me, shouting: 'March is here, and remem-ber the tortoise wins the race.'

Laughing, we tumbled into my room in halls and threw on dressing gowns, then you drove us to the one-bedroom apartment your father had bought for you. In the bathroom, you stroked my hair and kissed my head. I suckled your fingers. You licked my heel. I nipped your wrists. Water, turned wine-red with bath salts, lapped furiously at the side of the tub, landing in loud splashes on the black and white tiled floor. Afterwards, we wrapped ourselves in towels still stiff from the radiator and were solemn in our declarations of love.

Was it love? If only there were a test that could be administered to determine it. Would doctors track the heart rate (too fast) and pulse (it races)? Would neurologists monitor the mind for signs of distraction? Or psychologists analyse vocabulary, counting the number of times per minute the beloved's name appears? If science can measure the damage sustained by skin after exposure to sunlight, the effects of nicotine on an unclean lung, the loss of memory after an electrical storm, how is it that it cannot measure the impact of love on a soul that thinks itself immune? Yes, yes, it was love. That semester I learned about passion and painting simultaneously, until I became confused between the two realities. Were we the alabaster bodies, entwined and stretching into the lapis lazuli sky? Did we chase a dog's leg criss-crossed against an English field; mock fleshy mortals cavorting? Panic at the swell of a belly like a bowl? Lose ourselves in webs of lavender? We had only to speak of love and the room moved, a magic trick where it oscillated and we abandoned all attempts at logic. In those days, when we fucked, I imagined I was flying. I saw places in my head, aerially, tracing their contours delicately, as if reading in Braille. There were rugged patches of coastline, serrated as knives, and bumpy sand dunes. When I came to, and found myself once more on the crumpled sheets, my breathing furious, us sated, I felt some sadness.

Gradually, after weeks of living in the present tense, we introduced the past (perfect, imperfect and historic). You wept when you spoke of your English grandfather who was convinced he was the king of the Netherlands. Your grandmother decided to commit him to an institution in Bournemouth but he kept disappearing and going to London, where he would book entire floors of hotels for himself and his imaginary courtiers. After telephoning a series of orders to his good-natured friends, he commanded them to pick up the bill. (He was royalty and though cash is king, kings don't carry it.) When he died, you felt like the world became suddenly very dull. I confided in you that I have little memory of my childhood before the age of six. A family vacation in Toulouse which my mother Mercedes left abruptly. She took the car, intending to drive to relatives in Gaillac, but she never arrived. Lightning – rain in sheets – tangle of metal and charred flesh – ashes scattered in a field – dead sunflowers like brown and brittle fists, upright in rows in the hot August sun – new black velvet dress and black shoes that pinch – a speech (too long, I needed to pee). The coroner ruled accidental death.

'What does your father do?' you asked.

'He's a con man. Semi-retired.'

My father started young, inspired by the array of fake IDs for sale in Bangkok. When he returned to London, James Glass obtained the entire *Encyclopædia Britannica* with solid pine display cabinet for nothing – he was always a man who understood the value of knowledge. His first successes were importing faulty cuckoo clocks that only ever chimed at 4 a.m. and exporting Burberry goods with the checks askance.

He progressed to auctioning shares in phantom diamond mines buried beneath snowdrifts in Siberia. As a child, I took pleasure in the souvenirs he brought home from his mysterious business excursions. I especially liked the ink blotters, and the faux leather folders (embossed with gold, undulating writing, full of thick cartridge paper and envelopes) from a hotel on the shores of Lake Geneva. Sometimes he had an accomplice – the wife of an ice-cream manufacturer. Mrs W: slick and fuchsia and dark; her jewellery neat and golden.

'And your parents?'

'Lawyers,' you laughed.

Evenings, stoned, debating whether painting was dead; once, making our own small canvasses with oil paints and titles like *The Seven Signs of a Chameleon in Love; My Perfect Nosebleed*. We researched esoteric subjects like peculiar saints, and made them into our evil alter egos. After an argument, I named you St John the Dwarf (a vain and absent-minded man given to mood swings), and you retaliated by calling me St Lucy of Syracuse (a Sicilian virgin martyr often depicted carrying her own eyes on a platter). We pondered on the nature of clichés. What would they taste like if they were edible? Would they be bland or sour? Overly sweet? Could they be nibbled on, or did they have to be swallowed in their entirety like bitter medicines? We fashioned ourselves after the great romantic pairings. We said: we are as suited as Narcissus and the glassy water of a cool pool, or as perfect as a bisexual and a ladyboy.

We spent our summer in my father's house of mirrors by the sea. He paid you to forge seascapes. You two sold them to gullible Americans as Quiner O'Keeffe's recently discovered *Nothingness* series. We were on the beach when you suggested I move in with you. Pebbles, green-white on the shore and pewter sand sparkling our shoes. From a distance we might have been unsuccessful pirates: heads bent, hands in pockets for the robust silver squall of an English summer's day. As the seawater turned a dirty blue, we heard someone yodel, 'Tarquin! Tarquin! Don't forget the towels.'

When we graduated, we decided that we would go to Paris. We spoke of light and classicism; of *tricolore* flags relaxing against white masks and distressed eau de Nil doors. How did it happen that we slid? We started to blame one another. (Who's to say who was framed?) My memory is hazy; do not trust it. It is as if I recall myself underwater. I remember all your failings, yet mine seem inconsequential. I have taught myself this, instilled this fiction in my mind as schoolteachers have children learn by rote the names of prime ministers and the dates of wars.

It was my evening to cook. October, and unexpectedly cold rain was cascading, darkening the already cinereous sky. Sheets and towels I had washed the previous day were still heavy with damp. They were strung across surfaces — cupboard doors, backs of chairs, across the fold-up table — and you sighed impatiently at how they confined our space. There was little in the fridge but I was lazy and unwilling to leave the steamy warmth of the apartment. So I served what we had — all of it — on a plate: a roasted bulb of garlic cleaved in two; shiny hard-boiled eggs (whole, three each); a peak of white rice; and a slice of baguette. There was no wine, only milk. The following night, it was your turn to cook. You were reading Huysmans, so you prepared a meal where all the food was black (truffles, olives, grapes). You pondered aloud why it was that all the most expensive food was black. 'Maybe it is because it reminds us of death,' you opined. But I had seen the same movie, and was more impressed by it than you, and told you so. Gathering up the place mats made me think about the *place we were at*. The conversation turned to how much longer we were going to stay in Paris. You were tiring of our poverty, of having to draw caricatures for tourists with long noses and too-round faces. My photographs were black and white and mediocre.

'Then why don't we go somewhere else?' I complained. 'Berlin. New York.'

'You can't run away for ever.'

In a temper, I composed the last letter I ever wrote to you:

> *Sebastian,*
> *Don't gloss over the truth. This relationship is pointillist.*
> *You brush all my aspirations aside. You fill me with*
> *emulsion.*
> *Alice*

You ignored the note. The following day was a glorious Indian summer day.

'Let's walk?' you asked.

We walked from the Marais to the Eiffel Tower, strolling, hand in hand, stopping, laughing, leaning over bridges. The water blinked in the sunlight with the beginnings of autumn, leaves of raw sienna. I felt carefree, five years old again. (Red coat buttoned to chin, red mittens sifting wet leaves for newly fallen conkers. Glee at finding the ones still in their cases. Hoarding the polished orbs between woollen balls of socks. Then, revisiting them, always disappointed at how quickly they had lost their shine.) On the way back, we rested by the water and bought ice creams that purported to be genuinely Italian but were slightly chemical in taste. Mine was strawberry and yours pistachio, but you tipped your cone to lick the base and the ice cream fell out of it on to the pavement. We had a brief and sulky argument before bed, but fell asleep quickly.

Morning. The argument of the previous evening lingered in our mouths like nicotine. It was pouring with rain and even now I wonder how things might have been if the sun had woken us instead. Aren't there links between meteorology and mood? Is it mould at the end of the rainbow? Does lightning strike twice in the same heart? You are the sunshine of my strife . . . Or perhaps it was not raining (my memory is foggy), but I have chosen to remember it so. Neither of us wanted to apologise. You got out of bed, abruptly, and showered. I made myself a coffee, black and strong. Then I went downstairs to buy a newspaper. I came back and you were gone.

I was irritated all day. I imagined you in the Louvre, or walking Montmartre. Evening rain fell on asphalt. I began to worry. The police were unhelpful. They asked me if anything was missing from the apartment. They wanted a description so I told them of your soft features and easy wealth, of your eyes sharp as cut sapphire. Anything else? they asked, impatiently. When I opened the drawers by the side (your side) of our bed, I saw that your passport was gone. I wrote down all the possible reasons for your departure:

1. You were crazy. A rare disease had affected your brain. Following several attempts to escape the asylum, you were bound and straitjacketed.
2. You had been kidnapped by conceptual terrorists for crimes against painting.
3. You had amnesia. I was there, in your mind, somewhere, and you trying to remember my name or address was as vague and difficult as catching a fish with your bare hands.
4. You were dead. Your body was grume and vinegary, sunk beneath the green Seine. Death by violent misadventure; death by suicide . . .
5. You had fallen in love with someone else.

Your never answered your telephone. I left many messages. Some I wrote down first, they were composed and conciliatory; others were screamed in despair after I had drunk two bottles of red wine by myself. I waited in Paris. There were things you had left. Your cufflinks; a pair of boxer shorts. All your books and your clothes. It was your pâté de foie gras uneaten in the fridge, your paintbrushes, stiff and uncleaned. Paris seemed grey: the echoing ring of doomed bells; skeletal trees and skies blanched with cold. The weather was inclement yet I felt constrained to walk. Now I found the Paris of catacombs and beggared streets, of rats jumping thin rails to skirt the axis of this spit worn city. My eyes were caustic; my body abscessed. I collided with you – but not you – a stranger with the same gabardine coat; me, a blind moron, wearing my rage like a totem. I had a mantra: I will bite the head off a pigeon, I will roll a man in the palm of my hand, I will sever columns from temples, I will blow a house down, I will scatter you and hold you tight as iron filings on a magnet, I will drown in my own biliousness. I enacted scenarios. I wore a ballgown of crimson and a tiara of amethysts. I was enthroned when you reappeared. In my fantasies, you were always repentant. You were the beggar with bare feet, grimy blue. Maimed: blood seeped through your bandaged torso; your legs were splintered in several places. What temperature is grief? Is it burning, like scalding water that runs over and pulls at soft skin? Perhaps it is so cold it is sharp as ice cream caught on the edge of sensitive teeth. Maybe it is merely humid as the constant and predictable heat of a New York summer.

I decided to start taking photographs again. When I opened my camera case for the first time since your disappearance, I found it. Your reply. I have it still, as I have all your missives, wrapped in graph paper and tied with a black silk ribbon.

Alice,
Cheap shot. It came to me in a flash: you see everything in black and white! You blow things up out of proportion

*and zoom in on all my faults. Maybe you should
develop alone.*
Sebastian

After that, I had a pretend funeral. I wore Tyrian purple.
(A colour created by accident some time around 1500 BC.
Hercules' sheepdog was playing on the beach when it
crunched on a mollusc that dyed its tongue a superb violet.)
There was a tramp that occupied the bench at the corner
beneath a mural. I gave him your clothes and shoes. RIP, I
said. In the nineteenth century, convicts' bodies were flayed
after death. Here, in the twenty-first, we were both convict-
ed. We were bound in the death of our love affair: a skeleton
and an *écorché*.

Yet I was haunted by your note. For weeks I could not
sleep without nightmares. I saw newspapers six feet tall dancing in the snow; poisoned milk spilled on an ebony table; a
white sheep in a field of black sheep; a penguin playing the
piano; salt and pepper pots filled with cracked pearls.
Miniature zebras lay dead on zebra crossings.

THE GOOD LASS

ALLAN RADCLIFFE

I jolt awake with the growl of the taxi, blink into sharpness, squint up at the clock. Not even half twelve. He's back before last orders. His pals must have made their escape, left him prattling to himself, blissfully unaware. I'd been expecting at least another hour to myself before getting started on my bedtime routine.

While I've been dozing, my photo album has slipped to the floor. I shuffle forward, creak down, lift it on to my knees and prise it open for one last look over Anthony's eighteenth. All the photos have gathered higgledy-piggledy at the top of the page. I slide my hands under the plastic cover, feel the static pulling at the wee hairs at the ends of my wrists as I rearrange the pictures in square rows.

Anthony's white smile glints up at me. There's a couple of smashing group shots from the Park Bar where we had the party, and a lovely one of me and him together: just the two of us. People are always saying he looks like me because of the colouring, the fair hair and blue eyes, but I reckon he's got his dad's smile. I remember when I first met Tony the girls from work were always rattling on about his dark brown eyes and warm smile. Strong, white, even teeth. Not a beery leer. Not then. I'll phone Anthony in the morning. No, not in the morning. Tomorrow's Saturday. He gets cross with me when I phone him mornings and he has to raise himself from his pit to answer it. I'll wait till after lunch.

Downstairs, the engine rumbles into life. The yellow glow around the living-room window shivers off. I picture him, down in the street, head dropping lower and lower like an ice cream melting down its stick, thick, clumsy fingers rummaging for his keys in the pocket of his good Marks & Spencer suit jacket.

I clap the album shut and ease myself to my feet. Glance out the window. It was still light when I sat down. Last thing I remember was watching the lights click on one by one in the windows of the tenement block opposite. I just couldn't keep my eyes open. I seem to be doing that more and more these days – nodding off during the day, snoozing in my chair. I'm turning into an old woman. The living room's clean and tidy at least. Earlier on, I scooped the week's clutter into a bin bag, tied it up and dragged it down to the black wheelie bin. I dusted, polished and hoovered, pulled the head off the nozzle, ran it around the edges of the room, poked it into the furthest corners. I can't curl up and put the week behind me until the flat is spotless.

The stair door thuds shut, shoogling the whole house. He'll be making his painful progress up two flights. Slow, uneven footfalls, right arm outstretched, hand gripping the banister for balance, fringe flopping forward. I used to fret when he stayed out half the night and crawled in at dawn. These days I'm more likely to think something's the matter when he appears before I'm tucked up.

I go through to the kitchen. Tonight I treated myself and stopped off at a Chinese restaurant called Jenny's Kitchen on the way home. Carol from work recommended it. Carol hates cooking, eats out all the time. More and more I can see what she's on about. I cannot be bothered trailing around the supermarket, chopping vegetables and soaking and scrubbing pots when nine times out of ten it's just me fending for myself. The menu in the Chinese was enormous, full of things I'd never heard of, so I picked out dishes I remembered try-ing in the days when me and him still did things like eat out, go to the pictures, go to the dancing. I went for chicken with spicy leaves, boiled rice and a couple of spring rolls. Next time I'll be more adventurous. Back home I marched straight into the kitchen, dumped the blue carrier bag on the work-top, pulled out the stack of plastic tubs, poured the contents on to a plate and ate the whole slippery heap like a greedy child. You'd have thought I'd never seen food before. Delicious. Wait till I tell Carol. Once I'd finished, I filled the sink and washed up my plate, fork, knife and glass. I dried them and put them away. I cleaned the surfaces with Flash, swept and mopped the kitchen floor; left the lights blazing and the door wide to the wall so it would dry quickly.

His key's scratching at the front door, stabbing around for the lock. I can't even remember why I came through to the kitchen. I must be going daft in my old age. Oh yes. Put my pictures away. He's been getting impatient with me for spend-ing so much time with my old photos. Says I'm obsessing. Says now the boy's moved out I have to learn to let go a bit. I drop the album into a drawer, cover it with tubes of greaseproof paper, kitchen foil, cellophane, bang the drawer shut. I take a hold of the damp cloth that's hanging off one of the taps and give the worktop a quick once-over. I switch off the light and pad quickly through to the living room, drop into my armchair and squirm myself into a comfy position. I pull my legs up under my bottom. My ankle starts stinging so I slide my legs out from under me, stretch them out, one ankle crossed over the other. Pick up the remote control, aim it at the telly and try to look engrossed in the tail end of a BBC documentary about Israel and the Arabs.

The front door crashes home. He could never do anything quietly. Every night coming in he slams the door, even when it's dead late and I'm bound to be in bed. He's never made the effort to creep about. It almost makes me laugh now, remembering how I went through a steady spell of leaving notes half sticking out of the letterbox pleading with him to *please try and be quiet*, reminding him how badly I sleep. I haven't done that for ages. Before I moved through to Anthony's old room I would lie in the dark, listening to those great clumsy feet stumbling closer, the rattle of the key, the door swinging to the crash. I'd hear him clattering from the hall to the kitchen, raking through the fridge or gnawing on his fish and chips or kebab or pizza. I'd watch, my eyes raw, as he shuffled into the bedroom, danced out of his clothes, fell into bed, spread himself, spent the rest of the night rolling around, muttering and slurping. Sometimes he would touch his hand to my hip or curl his arm round my middle. I'd hardly ever reach back. I'd lie rigid in my corner of the double bed, watching the black disappear, my mind racing darkly. I vaguely remember a time when I would cling tight to his warm body until I fell asleep, but that was so long ago it might as well have happened to another person or somebody in a film. I can't remember the last time we had sex, the kind that leaves you sweltering, hot in the face, your heart thumping.

'Liz?' He's noticed the living-room light is on; a disruption from his bedtime routine right enough. 'Liz, you still up?' His voice staggers towards me.

The smoky pub smell floats into the living room before him. He bumps through the door and stops, head drooped forward, staring down his nose at me. Even before he opens his mouth I can tell he's steaming. His wee, round head balances above his unbuttoned shirt collar, the white face standing out against the black of his suit jacket. His eyes are wide open and full of red. The pupils have shrunk to the size of blackheads. He stands there, lips opening and closing like a guppy, tongue clicking off the roof of his mouth, teeth chewing air. A crumpled chip wrapper pokes from his jacket pocket.

'This is late for you.' He speaks very slowly and carefully. 'This is . . . past your . . . bedtime. I thought you'd have been in . . .' He jabs his thumb backwards. The speed of the movement makes his upper body sway about.

'Bed? Oh, I got completely engrossed in . . . um . . . this.' I nod my head at the telly. The documentary's been replaced by the titles of a late film. I feel along the arm of the chair for the remote and snap the screen dead.

As I turn my head back round I see him starting towards me for his kiss. His knee catches the edge of the coffee table and he stumbles, throwing both arms out to stop him landing face-first.

I wince.

'Jesus, Tony, are you OK?'

'Yeah, yeah, I'm fine,' he mutters, eyes screwed tight, trying to laugh off the sharp pain we both felt. I feel a rare heaviness at the back of my eyes. I can't help it; he can be so pathetic. He laughs again and bends to kiss me. The pale, waxy moon zooms in, all the pink squiggly lines coming into focus. The once-sharp angles of his face have long melted away. I avoid inhaling stale, beery breath by gently catching the back of his head and tipping it towards me. I lower my lips to his crown and exhale. His hair is no longer perfectly black. The sideburns are flecked with grey, white threads crawl all over the top and there's a bald spot that's only visible from above or behind. A slice of chopped pork on a bed of brown rice.

I pull away. He falls back into the other armchair. My stomach is making noises he won't hear: the Chinese floating around, settling itself. His head is back. He's pushing the flat of his palm against the space at the top of his nose between his eyebrows like he's pressing away the week's weariness. His work tires him out. He likes to unwind. It's the stress of the job. He's a manager in the back office of a bank. I have to say it makes me proud when folk ask me what he does and I tell them his title, though I couldn't tell you what he actually does with his day. I know he watches over a group of twenty people who spend their days punching clients' names, addresses and phone numbers into computers. He sets his staff their targets first thing and checks whether they've lived up to his expectations come half five. I imagine he spends the rest of the day drifting around the desks, chatting to the new recruits, especially the pretty young women, offering to fetch them cups of steaming dishwater from the machines or shouting them lunch in the subsidised staff canteen. It's always his round.

His flaccid second chin is pressed into his chest as if to quell the incessant hiccups. His shirt buttons strain against the round hump of his belly.

'Who was out tonight?'

'The usual crowd. John and Danny.' Then, almost as an afterthought, 'A few of the young lassies.'

'Where did you go?'

'The Marmion.'

'Oh, right. You're back early.'

'They were all a bit tired. Nobody wanted a big night.'

His pals must have drifted off home, abandoned him one by one. The thought of him holding court before a circle of empty glasses and chairs makes me feel sad.

'How's John?' I ask him. 'Has Lynda heard any more about her job?'

He lifts his head slowly, turns to look at me with disinterested eyes, prises his crusty lips apart.

'Yeah . . . yeah . . . she got a transfer to . . . Liverpool, I think it is . . . No . . . no . . . tell a lie: it's Blackpool. So they'll be moving down. End of the summer I think.'

'That's a shame.'

'Yeah . . . I'll miss John . . . He's a good lad.'

His head shoots straight.

'Any of that wine left?'

'In the fridge.'

I watch him rock back and forth in his chair until he's gathered steam enough to rise. He stands still for a moment to get his balance. I feel my whole body sag.

'I'll go,' I say, standing. 'You have a seat. I'll get us both a glass.'

'Good lass.' He raises his arm, holds out his puffy fingers to give me a clumsy squeeze on the shoulder as I sidle past.

'You hungry? Want anything to eat?'

He drums his fingers on his belly, eyebrows knitted as if mulling over a clue in a crossword puzzle. 'I'm OK thanks . . . I'm OK . . .' he says eventually. His eyes drift slowly down to his jacket pocket. Confused, he draws the chip wrapper out and glares accusingly down at it. I can't help having a wee smile to myself.

I wander through to the kitchen, pluck the lonely half-empty bottle of Chardonnay from the fridge. The cork is jammed right down the neck so I rake around in the drawers for the bottle-opener. I cringe, remembering the times I hid the alcohol so he wouldn't be able to carry on drinking when we got home from a rare night out. I remember frantically stashing bottles in cupboards, behind the furniture, under the bed. He would tear the house apart. I don't do that any more.

The cold, wet glass nips my fingers as I struggle to prise the cork from the bottle. That's us just a few days into September, but you can really feel it getting colder already. I think about our last holiday. Gran Canaria, six years ago. He recruited a whole squad of drinking pals at the poolside bar, entertained the hotel with his stories while I sat squeezed into the corner, teeth permanently bared, whirring my straw around in my vodka and orange. The recurring memory of him jumping into the swimming pool fully dressed on the last night of our holiday used to make me stiff with embarrassment every time it popped into my head. Thinking about it now, it doesn't bother me so much.

Truth is, nothing bothers me much these days. I just can't seem to get going the way I used to. Half the time I seem to be walking about in a daze. The week just drags on for ever. I've always been an early riser but some days I don't even want to get up out of my bed. Now there's no Anthony to see to in the morning, I've just got his pale face hanging over his breakfast cereal to look at. I've been to my doctor but he just wrote me a prescription for pills. He says plenty of people take them these days, it's nothing to be ashamed of, but I'm not sure about that. I've heard the pills give you bad side effects like losing your hair and making you fat. I'd hate to get fat.

The other day Carol caught me having a wee episode in the toilets. It wasn't my fault; I was that tired. She asked what was wrong and her face was that kind and concerned I couldn't stop the floodgates opening. I have to admit I wasn't very discreet. After I'd finished rambling, Carol guided me through to the staff room, sat me down, raised her thin, neat eyebrows, leaned over the low wooden table and told me I should think about leaving him. She said now that Anthony's off at university I've no real ties. I didn't know what to say. I was really embarrassed. I muttered something about the mortgage and the joint account and the cost of divorce but Carol just placed one smooth palm over my hand and said I could come and stay at hers. Carol has an answer for everything.

Carol told me to write him a long letter, leave it in the fridge clipped to a six-pack of Stella, then pack my bags. I'd never do that. I don't like the thought of him discovering a letter and reading it, taking it all in without knowing what to do and no right to reply. It feels terrible to think of him reading my letter alone. Anyway, what would Carol know about it? She has no time for relationships, doesn't understand commitment, insists she loves her own company, says the most generous thing her husband Jim ever did in twenty years of marriage was to drop dead from a massive heart attack. She didn't sound like she was joking either.

I'm just freeing the last bits of crumbling cork from the bottle when I hear his snores thundering through the house. I go through to the big bedroom – his bedroom – slide open the wardrobe doors, take a blanket from the top of the pile and go through to the living room. He's slumped in his chair. His jaw hanging open, mouth perfectly round, head pushed and pulled by his inflating, deflating chest. He's not for shifting. I cover him with the blanket. As I tuck it tight under his chin he stirs briefly, mutters something fairly insensible that ends with the word 'glass'. Or was it 'good lass'? I'm not sure.

He opens and shuts his mouth, shoulders sliding further down, head hanging off the back of the chair. I remember Anthony sitting at the kitchen table reading one of his music magazines, cheerfully telling me about all the pop stars who died from choking on their own vomit in their sleep: Jim Morrison and Jimi Hendrix and some stupid idiot from Led Zeppelin. All very ghoulish, I thought at the time.

The growling sets off again at the back of his throat. I stand over him, staring down at his fluttering tonsils. He could choke on his own vomit one of these nights if he's not careful. I stand there, mesmerised by that thought for what seems like ages.

Then I place my hands around his head and gently ease it forward until it's settled against the cushioned back of the chair. I touch my lips briefly to his smoky scalp before turning out the light.

This time I hear the watery croak through the dark.

'Good lass.'

Inside of a dog . . .

POETRY

POEMS
———

SARA BRYCE

First Time You Stayed Out Late

Fireworks explode the sky;
a crayon burst of fireworks
falling;

carried downstream
in shreds
over boulders, grasses.

Taste of bonfire is
everywhere;

flames licking night-scapes,
plaiting dirty strands
of smoke.

We're drenched by
sounds colliding,
spilling down the hill.

You're standing close,
watching me watch,
clutching my hand.

Shoulders pulled taut.

Eyes on fire.

Your expressions tiptoe after mine.

Calling from Sauchiehall Street

Coins can jam in the slots:
try coppers.

Silvers slip through,
counting down . . .

A crackle down the line.
Starched silence while I
wait for your voice:

broken;
strung out across distance reached
only by wires.

Not long awake.
Not yet watered, fed, brushed into shape.

I mouth shapes in the
darkness,
forgetting my lines now we're live.

You sigh, tut, demand
answers, names:
I hold my breath.

A stand-off.
Words recoil, burrowing out of my grasp.

Your tight-lipped calm.

We hang up together, on cue, under cover.

A Walk in the Rain

On days like these—
whip-lashed,
dark before the
clocks pass two,

we wore coats; hoods
cavernous under
a stoning of rain

heels pulling
straps of turf from
flat grass

legs and arms
shrink-wrapped in
breathless gusts

leaning into
shredded space
awash with sound.

See You off on the Train

Echoes skating marble, glass;
clack-track of heels fractures
crowds around us.

Sun-pooled floor up-lights
your lip, cheek, bone-cupped
rim of your eyes.

I hold your bag, watch
kaleidoscopes of
minutes

shrinking.

You breathe places;
plan in hoarse fog;

stamp your feet,
ticket sharp between
your fingers:

white sliver of distance.

Learner and Teacher

Your hands cup potatoes
flat-faced from the
heft of your knife,

shovel cubes and stalks
to wilt in the
thick-bottomed pan.

You let me hold the spoon,
two hands,
standing tiptoe on a chair,

rolling warmth of the broth
kneading into my clothes.

*

Yesterday
shapes, sounds;
another language.

Eyes dimming
you grappled to
map out the grammar.

Strings pulled straight-
edged notes from
the page.

Slow fingers between frets.

I let you hold the
plectrum,
strum the last chord.

To a Ploughman

GEORGE ANDERSON

Muckle owwer-familiar manny,
Panic in ma breast?
Ah've near shat ma breeks
an ah WILL shoot the craw sharpish
if its aw the same tae you.

It's nae the murdrin pattle
ah'm concerned wi.
Your kind never
mean the herm—
bit yirr clumsy:

Ploughin awa, nae a care,
wondrin where yer next ride's coming fae.
Waxin poetic each new bint,
nae paying attention tae yer knittin
or mindin fowks' hooses.

An thirr's heehaw, thank you very much,
tae start again wi.
Ah don't even know

what foggage green is, big yin,
bit thirr's nain.

Mibbes if ah wis a masonic moose
oan the squerr
ye'd see me richt:
A bit boxie in yirr cottage,
Puckle straw or comfy cloot,
Rind o cheese or crumb o breid,
Bit naw.

Yer feelin sorry for me noo
but at the back o yer heid
yer thinking:
'Poem fae this,
ya dancer.'

LORNA CALLERY

as

the man in the window
looking in

the white rabbit
a mere outline

fear filled
blank stare
eyes piercing
as if
into headlights

ears sharp on end

man's eyes
fixated
counting down the time

as
two letters inevitably rub shoulders
like
'a'
and
's'

he enters the space

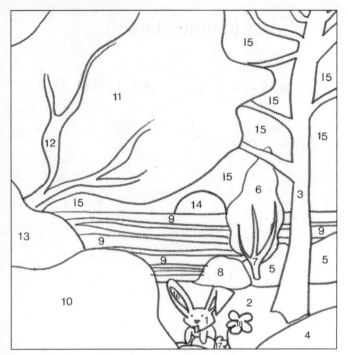

Remake the Narrative

COLOUR BY NUMBER

KEY:

1 – R	6 – E	11 – A	15 – T
2 – E	7 – T	12 – R	16 – I
3 – M	8 – H	13 – R	17 – V
4 – A	9 – E	14 – A	18 – E
5 – K	10 – N		

dust bunnies/Dyson

pot-bellied plastic dragon
inhale us

suction up the silence,
past days resting
on furniture and flat planes:

electricity pulsing
through acrylic veins

cyclone churning
stale air pumping

the latest model
for ethnic cleansing
eradicating memories
until the very last second

before the plug's metal limbs
embrace the socket

the night I wore
the geisha's face

oval moon

cheekbones lost in snowstorm

porcelain
interrupted by

painted brows
dark strokes
underlined   by lashes
thick and black

  dark
    eyes
sadness bleeding into
the powdered face;

brown ink on white parchment;

pale face
negative space
on to which
             project
the features you so desire

smile; perfectly placed

lips outlined with precision
Max Factor crayon No.12: FIRE
FLAME: No.948
sparking on ice

to press your lips against
could be fatal

set alight

the weight of a paint fleck or paint fleck waiting

stairwells tacked with
EXIT signs pointing
the wrong direction
picture framer's
woodchips turn to sawdust
scattered through the air

gloss grey emulsion reveals itself
between footprints
suicidal paint spats
floorboard grooves

white walls drip
ideas
this place sweats concepts
like Gallowgate men
spout sexist comments
fucking beautiful

turpentine entwined with pencil lead: 5B

the idea waits
in clear liquid
intoxicating space: DO NOT INHALE
a single fleck of white paint
on an endless white wall

a solitary fleck curling
like a tongue to the rain
attempting to break free
but it hangs there threatening

the artist
who is compelled
to taste it

the sinister little hammer decided to kiss the mirror once and for all

That night
smashed
into a thousand pieces
when I looked down
it lay shattered
at my feet

what once reflected
the world above
became oil spills of colour
bleeding through the edges

reality was melting

be like a machine
it said
a remote-controlled
yellow metal claw
industrial
efficient
busy
picking up the shards
each one heavy

concrete
back-breaking

well,
the machine is broken
sharp rubble stuck
to the floor
the pieces looking
more and more
like the pavement
every single day

MAGGIE WALKER

the garden

arriving in a grey-wet dawn I find
what nothing has prepared me to expect:
paint peeling from the gate like blistered skin,
exposed rust weeping,
hinges fretful with neglect
complaining late late

the path is choked with grass
white slabs turned grey
slugs' slime where marrows split across the ground
roses fuchsias foxgloves tightly bound
with tendrils of convolvulus
wasps feasting torpid on the apples' sweet decay

this patch of earth was his eden
nurtured loved
tended like a child
now autumn has strewn litter on the lawn
through broken glass the untamed vines run wild

Grandad's floosie

was she shadow-soft like velvet
like a warm night
with stars let loose
and the moon a fragile crescent
hanging small and so bright
in the darkness

was it pain to him
never again to lie
in the smooth scent of her skin
and watch how effortlessly
the cheap bangle he gave her
slipped over her delicate wrist

did he even once
see the child
none of us ever knew
or spoke of

May in England

this day is
a million bluebells
a million deep-scented
shivers of purplest blue
under tree shadows
where light darts

through an everywhere of green
a riot of bursting thrusting greens
tumbling over old walls newly warmed
great leaping festoons of green

beside shock-yellow fields of rape
quivering pale primroses
cowslips miracles of yellow

it is the frothing pink whiteness
of tissue blossoms
in gnarled orchards
snow blossoms drifting falling
white upon pink upon white

beneath skylarks high
in the invisible blue
new-washed sky

MARY SMITH

Sometimes

Sometimes when the phone rings
I hope it's for me:

imagine I'll hear long distance,
a familiar voice saying hello,
your ear-to-ear grin,
winging along wires overland,
underground
to find its echo in me.

But, because it's been too long,
because I've worried, fretted, wept,
imagined the worst
I'm sharper-voiced than intended.
I'm in Iran, you'll laugh,
in answer to my question,
or Pakistan, maybe Moscow,
which you call *Moss-cow*.

It's been so long since
Jawad's letter came,
trying to explain, meaningless phrases—
doing all we can, Red Cross searching,
trying jails, don't give up —
on the page one word,
Taliban,
stands out, says it all.
He'll call if they hear more . . .

Sometimes when the phone rings
I hope it's not for me.

Living with War

Either side of the valley
opposing groups of freedom fighters
command two mountain tops.
During daylight hours,
they rest behind rocky barricades,
plan night assaults,
their presence ignored in the village below.

Men follow the land's rhythms,
plough, plant or harvest wheat;
women milk goats, weave carpets,
share gossip and laughter.

Schoolboys wonder what use
spelling to a *mujahid*,[1] while girls
learn to sew, keep house,
sing songs at weddings.

At evening's swift darkening,
families gather, bread baked,
stories told, doors closed,
one by one lamps doused.
Then, tracer bullets arc
across night sky.
Children fall asleep
to Kalashnikovs' lullaby.

---

1 *Mujahid* – a freedom fighter

—

THERESA MUÑOZ

Clara Wieck's early impressions of Robert Schumann

Whose hair falls across
his forehead; whose voice
tells her brothers fairy tales;
whose rough outline
under a white sheet
is more of a clown than a ghost
as he wobbles down the hallway
at near-night, listening
to their pretend shrieks;

whose forehead forms a pitchfork
when pressed for an answer;
whose fingers grow black as he strains
all hours of the day
inking compositions for her father;
whose hands present a new waltz,
still wet with thought.

Clara's father disapproves

Wieck's hand points at Robert
like a gun, thumb quivering;

Clara's eyes, lily-green
and just as wet, look away

as Robert studies the wall
zig-zags in the paint.

Their secret weekend in Dresden
the cause of this chaos

(and somewhere in Robert
his mother dies again

last breath hoarse, her white nightgown
stained under the arms, her puddle-face).

Robert's hand on the door
is loath to pull the handle and turn

and leave her standing like that
next to him, the clear mist in her eyes
like his own.

Robert's separation from Clara

He writes of the white handkerchief
she waved from her window,
the cloth that landed at his feet like a dove.

He writes of the carriage that took her to
Dresden,
away from him. When his fingers stretched,
palms a perfect arc,
and her horse kicked mud
on to his jacket.

He writes of crouching outside her house
at dusk, grass high as his knees
as he listens for a chord played twice,
a clear 'Rob-ert!'

Robert and Clara's marriage

It's Robert's idea
the joint diary between them
he picks up a feather quill
and scrawls the date on the inside.

A symbol of our love he says
but she can't touch the piano

when he composes
he likes to live in a tomb
of deep invention.

Eyes closed and arms out
Robert imagines the silky whine of a violin,
an earnest clarinet, but hears only
Clara banging the pots
in the kitchen.
Who will be the musician?
At night he curls
like a question mark
against her body.

Winter in Russia means
fur caps and blankets, sleigh rides.
Clara counts the empty seats
at her concerts, forgets to smile after playing.
Robert, dizzy again, aches to compose.
The great bell tower saves them.
Before its white stone
they stand holding hands in the snow
feeling small and foreign
and needful of each other.
Sixty-four tons of brass bell
rings in the change.

Clara's pregnant

It's Robert's fault.
His face hung above hers.
He shut his eyes harder than usual.
Whoof, he breathed, collapsed.

She's too big to tour this year,
too much of a spectacle
to watch onstage,
her hands don't reach the keys.

Purple, smeared with wet, and slippery
during presentation,
she names him Ferdinand:
         meaning *brave*,
         an attempt to be.

Robert smiles when told,
happiest when she is at home.
A sticky business, taking care of five small children
and one grown composer
who insists on hearing voices

one year later
looking out the window
she compares the sound of applause

to distant ocean tides

Robert's delusions

the same loud note over and over
like someone hammering
a nail in the wall

a high b flat or d sharp
a mix between a woman's shriek
and horseshoes clacking on stone

Clara and the children open and close windows
place their ears to the dusty floor
for the slightest vibration

Here, he points to his temple. *Here!*

Robert draws his curtains in the daytime
lays back down

and closes his eyes against it
beat of his heart in his head

Marie Schumann's memories

She did not see her father leave
the house, wearing just a dressing gown

she runs to the village, to the river
rain stinging her bare knees

and finds him dripping, with the two men
who fished him out the Rhine.

Marie can see a black carriage
come round the corner

and someone says he will be back, cured
but the servant girl starts to cry

        in her life
everyone will tell her
the story again:

how he offered his kerchief
at the river's tollbooth

threw his wedding ring into the Rhine
then waded in slowly
sure-footed amongst the stones

Clara misses Robert

If there exists another way
into the gardens

where you are walking
along a stone wall
level to your chin

if there is entry
to your ward's three rooms
your piano unused

if into your hand
exists a weight
to keep your fingers
from spilling all contents
to the floor

if there is another way to reach you
besides notes and messages
sent slowly by post

Clara in old age

An ordinary day, late April
her grandson fixed at the piano

playing Robert's F-sharp Romance
an old favourite, each note

a tiny glowing pyre
lit these forty years.

Briefly she conjures Robert's slim hands
and slow smile, his closed eyes

    until a cool shimmer
    curtains her lips

her cheek frozen in pose
her hand sliding down

    and down, almost touching floor
    fingers curled against the cold.

it's too dark to read.

Groucho Marx

Novel
Extracts

Burns
(extract from a novel in progress)

Eleanor Thom

Some heelabalow! Mammy mutters that she's not waiting up for him. She has a sore head. His dinner's left out though, like always, and the fire's still hissing in the grate when we go to bed. Rachel and me curl together at the bottom end, under our own itchy blanket. Mammy and May sleep the normal way. I lie wide awake, listening to the rain. It's soft except when the wind blows, and then it's like seeds scattering. It leaves long spitty droplets on the window, jewelled earrings. I've a pain in my stomach, wishing I could eat some biscuits, but I don't know where Mammy put them, and I'd be in bad trouble if I ate someone else's share. There's a dry crust, wired into the mousetrap. But I'll no go near that. That's dirty. I roll over and stare at the ceiling.

You hear the mice scrabbling as soon as everyone shuts up and stops rumbling about. So the trap's set in front of the fire each night, and usually it's been tripped by morning. You'd think they'd learn, wouldn't you? They never do.

We're studying a poem by Robert Burns at school called 'Tae a Moose'. I'm reading a couple of verses at the public speaking contest. Miss Munroe told me to sound like I really care about the wee mouse. I'm a good speaker usually, but I'd rather do a different poem. When I read this one out, all

I can think of is Daddy setting the trap. And I think of the mornings, when I watch him wiping mouse guts off the wire.

The trap goes SNAP! Almost cuts the mouse in two. Other times it's still wriggling when we get up. Sometimes you think it's dead and then it moves its tongue or a paw, slow and painful, sad-looking. Like it knows. Daddy beats the live ones with the poker, and I have to turn away. When I look back he's swinging them by the tails, lifeless as bootlaces. He slings the dead bodies on the fire and the flames dart up and eat them, like in hell.

Daddy's boots come pounding up the stairs, back from the McPhees'. I know there's a mouse already caught in the trap. The spring released just a few minutes ago. CRACK! Same sound as the belt sailing down on Bertie Topp's spit-clean palm. He's always getting it. I've only got the belt once so far. I scribbled on another girl's slate when she went to the toilet 'cause her handwriting was neater than mine was.

We don't get hit at home. Granny says the men can pummel their fists at each other all they like, but they'll no put a hand on a wean while she's still got a breath in her body. Daddy still tries to get me when I'm cheeky mind, if Granny's not looking. He can catch Rachel, but I'm too fast.

My heart starts to beat heavy in time with Daddy's footsteps. I know there's going to be trouble. We had two policemen round looking for him after what he did to that man's wall. Granny whispered, *Shaness!* She had to lie. She said he was out of town, and no, we hadnae a clue where he was. Of course I knew, but I kept my gob shut tight. Not a squeak when that lot come a-sniffing.

I fled round the back. Daddy was there with the McPhee men. We cry them 'Spotty McPhees', and they cry us Whytes 'Plugs'. I don't know why, it's an old traveller thing. They were chortling and snorting and pink with laughing, like a sty of spotty potbelly pigs right enough. I never play with the McPhees. Daddy was taking a swig from a bottle, and no one even noticed me in the doorway till twice I said, *It's the hornies looking for you, Daddy*, and one of they McPhees said, *Aw fuckin' hell*, and another told me to *Get away back*. I guess they hid him after I was away, but they needn't have bothered. The police only searched Granny's room, emptied the contents of her wardrobe on to the floor as she watched, wringing her hands on a shirt she was mending. They tipped the table and broke a mug that was set there. Warm tea splashed on to the floor, and like Granny said, there was no need for that. No need at all. Not when you could see fine that Daddy wasn't under the table. Not even a cloth on it. They smashed a bowl against the wall, and the glass shattered right by Big Ellen's head. Granny said it could have brought her baby early with the fright.

The footsteps are uneven, like he's planting his feet in a snowdrift. That means only one thing. I wish he would just collapse on to the wee sofa. Sometimes he gets fired up at Mammy for no reason at all and sends her out to the landing where it's freezing, no letting her in and crying her bad names.

The door slams. Mammy sits up. She must've been lying awake too.

Jesus, Duncan, keep it down, the girls are sleepin.

I close my eyes till I'm just peeking through the lashes, and keep as still as I can, playing dead lions. Mammy gets to her feet and the two of them pace round and round the table where the Tilley lamp's set, glowering like they're in the ring, each eyeing the other, sizing for a fight. Can Mammy no see he's in a bad mood? Why can't she leave it till morning?

We've had the police here, are you proud of yersel? Out getting peevie.

Daddy struggles to rip his coat off, and when he gets his arms free he throws it. The coat scoots over the floor and I hear a button skiting, a noise like a rolling marble. The coat hits the door and crumples, the cloth ruching up, as if it's run away from Daddy and now he's got it cornered. There's nowhere for it to go, except press itself into the wall. That's how Mammy stands when he shouts. She pulls her arms to her chest and holds her hands over her mouth. Her fingers clutch at her chin like a wee mouse's paws.

He shouts something I don't understand.

DO YOU KNOW? DO YOU? EH?

It's questions Daddy shouts mostly. No one ever says anything 'cause there's no answers.

AH DON'T . . . AH . . . AH DON'T . . . NOT A FUCK . . . NOT A FFF . . .

He stumbles to the fireplace. I wonder what's coming. I open my eyes wide, and through the shadows I see him pick something up. The mouse dangles by the tail, still alive, still caught in the contraption. Daddy brings it level with his face, fixes it there, laughs. The mouse twitches and its paws race hopelessly at the nothingness of the air. Daddy takes the poker. With each swing, a curse word. Is he crying too?

But he doesn't get the mouse. It's flying back and forth like a pendulum, and every time the end of the poker comes towards it I think, surely it'll be goodbye wee timorous cowrin' beastie this time. But Daddy tilts sideways with the motion, off-target. Misses every time. He tries a couple of swings again, more concentrated, making an animal kind of groan. First the poker goes too far to the left, then just below. His whole body's off-kilter.

Put the poker down, Duncan, put that thing down.

Mammy's begging scared, but I think he looks funny. I'm nearly giggling. Daddy wobbles back, like he's going to fall over his heels, and the poker drops from his fist. On the uneven floor, the handle starts trying to get away from the pointy end. It turns nearly a whole circle.

Daddy puts the hand that held the poker on the wall. Quietly then, he holds the wee mouse an inch over the hot embers. It takes me a while to stop smiling, like my mouth doesn't know which way to go. Part of me wants to grin, bare my teeth. My eyes peel, wider and wider as the mouse hangs in the red glow. It tries to rear back from the heat. I hate him then. I hate Daddy for doing that to the wee mouse. I imagine the raw burning on its nose, the fairy-thin paws, dry pain in its eyes. And I've my own pain, wanting to cry but my eyes too skinned, too watching.

This is how ah feel, Martha. Do you see that?

But Mammy's covering her eyes. He finally kills the mouse, beating it with a dead thud on the hearth. And then there's no sound except Rachel and May snivelling.

He slumps into a chair. That's it, I think. Mammy will

come to us now, and he will stay there a while before crashing on to the sofa. I start crying. Big tears fall from my cheeks and into Rachel's hair. She's tucked her face into my neck and I hold her tight. It's gone quiet. Why doesn't Mammy come?

I look. The pair of them are cheekie-for-chowie, him still sitting in the chair, head bowed like we do in assembly, face in his hands. Mammy stands, wrapping her arms round his shoulders, stroking his hair like she does us.

More tears run down my cheeks. Big raindrops on the window. I gulp and press my face hard into the mattress while Mammy takes his boots off, undoes his trousers and puts him to bed on the sofa. She sighs as she kisses him goodnight.

You'd think nothing had happened the next morning. No one mentions anything, except for the fine to pay the man whose wall got smashed, even though the man owed us really. Granny says we'll all pull together. She tells Mammy not to worry. *Watch yon daddy of yours,* she says on the way to school with me. *No better than a kinchin hisself, needs someone looking after him. Pity Duncan's no got a heid on his shoulders like Jock. Oh me!*

At wee break, Sandra comes over. *Betsy, are you wanting ma apple core?* I've not eaten a bite since yesterday. But I swallow and say, *No thank you.* She shrugs, kicks the apple core, and I watch it bounce and somersault over the ground to near my feet. Gravel sticks into the flesh like a grazed knee. *The animals will eat it,* she says, and I watch her go back to her friends, red shoes skipping.

I dread doing 'Tae a Mouse' all day. Even after lunch my

belly churns at the thought. We get mathematics, a dictation and handwriting. But I'm lucky. No poetry. When the final bell goes it's like a weight's been lifted. All the way back to the lane I skip, swing my satchel, and my kilt goes swish-swish over my knees. When Mr Vaccari passes he smiles and I sing inside.

> *Here comes Anton-eeoh,*
> *selling ice cream-eeoh.*
> *Tuppence a con-eeoh,*
> *Four pence for more-eeoh.*

I find Rachel sitting at Granny's table. No one else seems to be around.

Where are they?

Drying green. Will you play with me, Betsy?

Okay, I say, thinking hard. It's funny having a wee sister sometimes. She'll do daft things just 'cause I tell her to. Once I got her into the shop asking for *cinaminaminamin balls*.

Let's pretend to be Daddy, I decide, and she laughs. I make my feet go 'clomp . . . clomp . . . clomp' on the floor, and bash my fist on the table making as sulky a face as I can, *a mou ye could tie a string roun*, Granny would say.

Daddy's boots are by the door.

I've got an idea.

I twiddle the end of a lace round my index finger, the boot hanging down.

Look, I go. And I lift it over the fire.

That's cheeky, Betsy. You shouldnae do that.

Shut up, cowardy.

The boot smokes and a foul smell comes off it. That'll teach you, I think to myself. The flames dance around and lick at the toe part, which soon goes all black. I pull it out to inspect. Rachel wants a look too. She peers at it over my shoulder. A bit of the sole's gone crispy and the stitching there's come loose. I wonder if it's really going to hurt him, me doing this to his boot. Granny would think so. I hope he stubs his toe. A wee tinker's curse.

Okay, I say, flinging the boot down. *It's your turn.*

AH CAN FUCK! FIGHT! AN HAUD A CANDLE TAE ANY MAN!

I belly-laugh just like Granny to hear my wee sister shouting that over and over. She stomps about the room with one foot inside the other boot, the unburnt one, and she's facing me at the fire, shouting it one more time, loud!

When suddenly the door opens.

Daddy.

Rachel spins when he slams the door and she almost falls over. I see his hand grab her wrist, and I plant myself on the burnt boot, wishing Granny was here, looking for somewhere else to hide it.

But Rachel's laughing.

She's got her hand in his, spinning round and round like a windmill. And he's being stupid. He pretends to reach over to skelp her, and lifts his foot like he's giving her a kick up the arse. His toe disappears under the hem of her skirt, but she just squeals, louping forward, spinning and spinning till they're both exhausted.

What about my other wee girl? Will she no play with me any more?

Daddy, I mumble. *We had an accident.*

I can't look him in the eye as I take the horrid charred thing from under me. Rachel, who I think had forgotten for all the fun she was having, goes very quiet. So does Daddy for a while.

Girls, he goes at last. *These are no mine. They're your Uncle Jock's boots. You'd better find him and say sorry. Tell him I'll fetch another pair from the rag store. Don't look so glum, ah'm sure we'll find some.*

It's true. Daddy's wearing his boots, identical brown ones. I feel rotten. I hold the burnt boot really close, like it's a wee animal itself, and I can hardly look at Rachel. My lovely Uncle Jock! The boot's a part of him. It's like that with people's things, especially their clothes.

I can't stop sobbing when I see Jock, sitting on his bed reading a comic, wiggling his toes, not knowing at all that I've doomed him. He seems nicer than ever. That means Granny's right! There's an evil curse over him and it's my fault!

What's got into you, wee Betsy? Jock says. *Crying like that for an old boot! Have you lost your senses, darling? That can be mended, don't you worry. Uncle Jock's got loads o' pals, and one of them's the sooter at the top of the lane. He can sort this in two tics. Don't be daft. Dry your eyes, you silly bam.*

I start to feel better. Just a wee bit better. And soon it's fine, as long as I don't look at the cursed boot. I put my arms round Jock's neck and pray for him to be saved.

When Daddy comes back he's got shoes. Not new ones, but they're fine. Sort of slip-ons with no laces.

That's me, Jock says. *A wee bit on the large side, but no matter.*

You can wear two pairs o' socks, Daddy goes. If I had money I'd buy Jock a good pair of socks.

It's peaceful that night. Daddy stays in and plays with us, and that makes Mammy happy. She sings to May, who gurgles, and in between she does nothing at all but sit and watch. I get shunted on to the sofa to sleep and Daddy takes my place in the bed.

Late at night, and there it goes again. CRACK! Another poor thing in the trap. As I listen for signs of life, the poem starts up in my mind.

> *Wee, sleekit, cowrin, tim'rous beastie,*
> *Oh, what a panic's in thy breastie!*

The voice won't hush. So quiet and caw canny as a wee mouse myself, I tiptoe over the boards, two-by-two to the trap.

I go down on my hunkers. The fire's dead, and the cold makes all my wee hairs prickle. I tuck my chin inside my nightshirt, up and over my nose, and blow warm breath on my chest. My eyes peer over the top of my collar, watching the mouse. It's alive! Caught only by the tail. Just like the night before. You'd think they'd learn, really you would!

I pick up the mouse and the trap like it was a hot cinder, go to the blocked hole and pull the fistful of cloth away. My hands wrap round the creature, making a wee circle with it in the middle. Light streams through the boards from Uncle Jock's room. He must be reading again. Holding the mouse near a crack, I can see the panic it has taken. Its tiny ribcage shudders with fear. Its wide eyes are black, shiny as wet liquorice drops, ears stiff, and the skin inside as smooth and bluey-thin as drowsy May's eyelids. I even feel the fluttering heartbeat.

I keep myself steady, trying not to shiver, and whisper a verse of the poem. As my legs go numb I feel more of what's between my hands, the whiskers tickling my fingertips, the sleek surface of the tail, the nose trembling like a tiny pink flower.

I free the trap.

Like a shot, the mouse darts from my hands, straight into the hole. He's away to his warm nest. But I sit there a while longer, smiling so wide it's like my lips are tweaking my lugs.

VINCENT WELLS

We should have been easy enough to teach, empty vessels that we were, but Mr MacLean suffered with his nerves and couldn't hold a course. A see-saw of a man and vain, he made interminable, incomprehensible digressions into his private life in lessons, enjoyed slapping us around, pulling us out of our chairs and choking us with a twist of our collars in his bony fist, loved putting the ruler across the back of our bare legs. His behaviour worsened once he'd begun courting Miss Erin. She played with him, cat and mouse, until she'd pulled out his stuffing. He'd sit lost in thought, hair awry, tearful, grinding his teeth, or leap from his chair, bound over and shake one of us by the shoulders: 'What did you say, boy?' You wouldn't think to look at her. Her voice was melodious but her heart cold. She enjoyed our tears and knocking out the little blocks that shored us up, an absolute tartar when it came to spelling and pronunciation, and like Mr MacLean most irregular in her confidences. One day early in their courtship, I was standing by her desk for correction. She closed my book, laid a hand soft on my upper arm and said:

'Edward, my complexion is called peaches and cream. Do you think it a fair description? I mean, can you see where it is peaches and where it is cream? Speak up.'

'I think so, miss.'

'You think so? Shall I spell it out for you? No, you must know things for yourself, so you must think about it . . . A change of subject. Tell me, how is Mr MacLean today?'

He was worse than usual, wild-eyed, distracted, his mind racing at full throttle, he'd confessed to being at his wit's end to the whole class. He'd nicked his Adam's apple badly while shaving, the blood had bloomed on his shirt collar and with a really wild swallow the wound reopened.

'I think . . .'

'You do a lot of thinking, Edward. A lesson off the curriculum but one you should remember – a man must have conviction, must be capable of imprisoning a woman in arms of oak. He should have the strength to press her like a flower into the book of his heart. The feminine principle is water, the male fire, and love, the ideal result of their meeting, should be a great cloud of steam. Alas such things are rare . . .'

She tailed off, leaned back in her chair and looked out the window at the low grey sky. It was a humid day building to thunder, the air a warm wet cloth over your face. I had a longing for sleep. Miss Erin's shoulders rose and fell with a prolonged sigh. It slipped evenly from between her half-closed lips and mingled with the first distant rumblings from above. A bead of sweat, dislodged from the hollow at the base of her throat, dropped into the dark cleavage of her large bosom.

He sent her notes torn from the blank pages of our workbooks when the mood for composition struck him, forced them on us with shaking hands. We'd head off with him watching, nodding unconsciously, eyes shining bright with hope and a touch of madness. I couldn't resist reading the first one he gave me: *'You despise me. I love you. You would stamp on my face. I kiss your foot. You spit on me. My burning flesh is momentarily quenched. I love you still more. O Rose, thou art sick.'* I got a taste for more, made it known that I was prepared to pay a tidy sum to anyone who would bring me one of his notes, either a small fleet of sherbet flying saucers, a liquorice pipe or a half-packet of sweet cigarettes. The cigarettes proved far more popular than the pipes or saucers, particularly with the girls. I had trouble supplying enough.

I'm sure I would have been found out were it not for the facts; his messages were mostly rhetoric. Her indifference negated the rare one that required a reply, and with his fragile pride he wouldn't dare ask. I kept them for a long time. They were eventually lost in a move but not before I'd memorised the best of them. Among my favourites were: *'Thou art Dawn, peel back the cloak of my dark night and with thy rosy fingers pluck out my heart . . .'* or *'You condemn me, from darkness into the path of darkness must I enter . . .'* or *'I can't go on like this. Come to me as you said you would or I shall put an end to the charade once and for all'*, and for me the finest example of his art: *'I once could not think of what is not but now I welcome death. I shall fall the nine days to Tartarus singing your name.'* Here I was introduced to that fabled place for the first time. My imagination was seized. Nine days falling, the smash when you landed must have been formidable.

Poor Mr MacLean in all that chaos of affection, trying to fill our empty heads, leading us away from the simple pleasures of the alphabet and numbers, towards the stink of combustion, coal, hydroelectricity and the circuit, the signs of our mechanistic civilisation, industry, and to my place in that vast hell. He stood over the two of us.

'Paul, Edward, do you think you can make a battery-powered bell in the summer holidays? A little project, something to keep you from mischief.'

Before we could respond, the bell rang. Mr MacLean dashed back to the front of the class. There was a flash of lightning outside, a short delay then thunder crashed down. The windows rattled in their frames.

'Right, all the boys, up, up. Come on . . . We're on borrowed time.'

We did as he asked. It threw the girls into relief. At that time there was no real difference, not to me. I was an egalitarian: girls, boys, animals, men, women, machines, trees, all were one. The storm broke. Rain poured from the sky. We stood in silence listening, turned to look as the light outside went to pieces. The rain slid down the glass in sheets, cast the distorted daylight in a liquid film on everything in the room.

'Now, if you . . . ah . . . Quietly . . . yes . . . quietly, to the hall. No talking . . . and no coughing . . . not yet . . . save your breath . . . ha, ha, ha, ha, ha!'

His false, chopping laughter followed us out. A line of boys snaked the length of the hall. The head of this curious reptile disappeared into the mouth of Miss Francis's classroom and the hard-boiled old spinster stood guard outside. The crying of a child could be heard through the drumming rain. Our speculations were in whispers and our fears mounted as time passed. Moving over the highly polished wooden floor our shoes squeaked like mice. Every few minutes a boy came out with shoulders down and his head bent. Another would go in and we moved on. The rain increased in its intensity. The snake had been almost entirely swallowed before the overheads flickered into life, their light an uneasy, feverish yellow. When Paul came out with tears in his eyes my heart flipped. By the time Miss Francis tapped me on the arm, I was close to panic.

'In you go, Edward.'

Looking up for the first time into her red raw and hairless face I saw that she had for some reason overlooked pencilling in one of her eyebrows that morning. It gave her an unhinged look.

'Edward, wake up! Go in.'

Fitful daylight stirred the room. The desks and chairs had been cleared to allow a narrow channel from the door to the open space before the blackboard, where two men wearing white coats had turned to look in my direction. Both were middle-aged, both balding, but there the similarities ended. The one seated behind Miss Francis's desk with a sheaf of papers in front of him and a pen in his right hand was very thin. The other man, very large and turning to fat, sat awkwardly on one of our chairs with his knees forced up near his chest. He washed his hands thoroughly in a white enamel dish set upon the small desk to his left, dried them on a towel and beckoned me forwards.

'Approach.'

I reduced the distance between us, my little heart ready to burst, looking out for any machine that they might try and use on me, but I saw nothing out of the ordinary in the room.

'You are . . .?'

'Eddie Pullman, sir.'

I liked giving my full name, the pair of twin syllables, the even stresses. I preferred Eddie to Edward but either was OK. It beat most names I knew. I would say it over and over on the way to school when I had nothing to think about.

'Get up on the chair.'

I found the courage to ask this stranger a question that had been troubling me for a long time: 'What have I done?'

'Who can say? But you've done something. I find all boys have something to confess.'

The thin one commented, 'There is always your Original Sin.'

He laughed hard, put a hand to his chest, theatrically calming himself. The fat one turned in a confined way, looked at his companion. Their eyes met briefly and mutual appreciation passed between them. Turning back, my interrogator took off his glasses and rubbed his eyes a good while. He moaned soft beneath his breath. The liquid in them clicked and squintched. By the end of his ministrations he looked like a nocturnal animal caught out at sunrise, a baffled bear – beneath his eyes, like purses for tears, a pair of swollen watery bags, the dark skin stretched paper-thin and shining delicately in the washed-out light. He winced, turned again to his companion as if he'd forgotten something, his voice petulant.

'Mr Stubbs, do you really need that chair? Could I not have it for a while, have a turn with it?'

Stubbs didn't look at his colleague, but turned to address the window and the rain running down the glass, his voice melancholy.

'Is it to be a matter of turns or fit? The chair and the desk go together, they suit each other. A smaller chair will put the desk level with my eyes and I'll be unable to see the paper on which I'm supposed to write. What's the point to this if I cannot write down the results?'

'I feel stupid. Besides, it's my knees.'

'Have a stretch for God's sake, Mr Calder. You're always the same. You don't take care of yourself, you overeat, you drink too much every night, you've only recently given up your pipe.'

'It's something.'

'But hardly enough, a finger in the dyke, Mr Calder, a finger in the dyke.'

'My metabolism is against me.'

'How often have we had this conversation? You're in a loop. Just have a stretch and let's get on.'

Calder did as suggested. From that cramped position it took him some time to unfold. He twice let out a sharp grunt and winced with every ratchet click of his joints. He'd been sitting a long time and the knees of his trousers remained stretched out of shape. Putting both hands in the small of his back, he pushed his stomach forward, his head back. His spine went off like a string of crackers and he screamed. After this he appeared relieved and his voice cheered up considerably.

'By Christ you're right, Mr Stubbs. As usual. Sometimes I think I must be an idiot. And so . . . back to business.

Young sir, please, if you would, get up on the chair and let us get on.'

I intended to defy him but couldn't think how, or what to say to prolong the moment. I saw no point in reasoning my position. I was too small to struggle with authority. But nothing is entirely negative. I saw it was only a question of will and once I'd dispensed with it I felt as light as a cork. All that was to happen would. I climbed on to the chair, already turning it into a bold, adventurous undertaking. Calder squashed himself back down into his seat, smiled and loudly chocked his tongue.

'Good boy. Take your trousers and your underpants down.'

I couldn't stop myself. I began to cry. Calder showed some patience, let me get it out, likely calculating my tears would help reconcile me to the situation. After a few heaving sobs they did. Again, having no choice made it easier to do as he requested but I was surprised, for once underway it felt only a mild embarrassment, and carried a strong urge for comradeship in its wake. I undid my shorts, let them fall round my ankles but could go no further before clearing something up.

'Are you going to inject me?'

'With what?'

'Germs.'

'I mean with what equipment? Do you see a needle? But no, God, we're only concerned with whether or not your testicles are down, and if they are, for Mr Stubbs here to take note of their position. For the first and last time in your life, unless you are unlucky enough to develop cancer in one of them, you are the possessor of statistical testicles . . . so don't go on . . . be proud, take your pants down and we'll be done in a shake of a lamb's tail.'

He winked, waggled his little finger at me. I clenched my teeth. My bottom lip and chin still quivered and a metallic current trickled through the muscles of my throat, but I was warm from my crying jag, and knowing I was not going to be injected with germs lulled me further. My heart came out from under its stone. I put my thumbs in the elastic of my pants and pulled them down. As the air pressed on my buttocks and thighs and curled about my penis, my heroism came to an end. I knew what I had done. Such exposure between a child and a man was, and always would be until kingdom come, pure misery. Calder leaned in close. He smiled but the blue-black stubble covering his upper lip and jaw made him look hungry and desperate. His breathing was heavy. I could smell egg and onion badly covered by peppermints. When he saw my penis his eyes lit with interest.

'Mr Stubbs, some news. We find the boy is circumcised.'

'Say what?'

'A circumcision.'

'Circumstantial?'

This seemed an old, familiar routine of theirs.

'I've no idea, sir. Shall I ask him?'

'Yes, but get to the point.'

Calder looked at me squarely but with a flicker of amusement in his eyes.

'We don't see many occurrences of this in the suburbs. How did you come to be so unadorned?'

I have never been discreet and the facts of the case were something of which I was tremendously proud. My voice was a brass trumpet in reply. I think I may have even raised my head.

'I was born without a foreskin. My grandmother says I was circumcised by God personally and that it's a divine matter.'

This statement seemed to give Calder some displeasure. He sucked on his teeth and eyed me belligerently.

'Oh, she did, did she?'

'Yes, sir.'

It was true, not the bit about God but my condition at birth was genuine and rare.

'You are Jewish?'

I was afraid to say yes. I was aware of history. I lowered my gaze and waited. Calder didn't pursue the matter.

'Well, take your little miracle and hold him out of the way for me.'

Partially immunised by the grandeur of my revelation, I took the head of my penis between my thumb and forefinger. It shrank away from me. I pinched it harder so it wouldn't slip from my grasp and raised it up. It put me in mind of holding my nose closed above a spoonful of foul-tasting medicine.

Calder spoke softly: 'Don't mind me.'

I felt his cold, damp hand slide beneath my scrotum and cup me there. He looked at me dispassionately. I experienced a strong desire for my mother's presence, her warm embrace.

'Open you legs a bit . . . Good. Cough. And again. Harder. One more. Good.'

He rooted around between my legs, pressing up into my cavity, poking about a good while before he spoke.

'Cryptorchid, Mr Stubbs. We have one.'

They laughed together. Stubbs noted the figure down then addressed Calder in a smug tone: 'One could've guessed.'

They stared at me. Calder, his hand still under my scrotum, asked, 'What is it you find so unsavoury that you must hide your little balls away?'

I had no idea and shrugged. I wanted him to take his hand away. A newsflash came in over the airwaves: 'BOY-HERO CUTS OFF CRIMINAL LUNATIC'S HAND'. It wasn't going to be true. I didn't have my Swiss Army knife on me. It lay on the shelf above my bed, a paperweight on top of my magazine collection. I concentrated on my room, saw myself standing on my bed as I reached up, one hand on the Artex wall for balance, felt my hand close round the knife as Calder spoke again.

'Well . . . we can use our imaginations. When were you born, day and month?'

'February, sir, the fifth.'

'Aha, Aquarius.'

Calder leaned forward and said, 'It's so often the sign.'

'Of course, Mr Calder. A dreamer. *Alles ist klar*, as they say in the fatherland. Well, get yourself dressed, Eddie, we're done with you.'

He withdrew his hand with a quick grimace, washed fastidiously while I did as he asked and got down from the chair. I leaked a little urine into my pants. The brief flower of warmth was a victory. While Calder took care to dry his hands, Stubbs wrote out a brief note, put it in an envelope and handed it to me.

'Give this to your mother. You do have a mother?'

'Yes sir. Her name's Mrs Pullman.'

'Well, give it to her. It explains what she must do with you and your two little secrets. Now, off you go.'

GHOST WALKING
(extract from a novel in progress)

HANNAH RITCHIE

Waking up was difficult. Slow consciousness breaking into realisation and the opening of a single eye.

The drug had drowned her in sleep. Uncomfortable, heavy sleep that pushed her deep into the mattress and wrapped the sheet round her body like a shroud.

The insomnia had taken its toll and she had surrendered. There were no dreams, no twitching legs as the drifting began. Just fake slumber.

Past nights spent awake had become so regular. Three-o'clock rising. Doing last night's dishes, the ironing, the dusting of the ornaments, one by one in the glass-fronted cabinets. She thought the routine would kick in, even after the pills had dissolved in her belly. She imagined herself sleepwalking.

A ghost.

Sadie was heavy, groggy, her head aching. She sat up, pushed one leg out of bed, feeling the cool floor. A milky film covered her lips. Sleeping with her mouth open was a new thing. It made her tongue dry and rough and speech was impaired, unusual to begin with; it did not sound like her. She tested it. 'Sadie, Sadie,' she said. It was not her.

Her sense of smell was fading. As if she had a cold. She had started to buy huge bunches of flowers from the man in the market. Lifting them sopping wet from the buckets he offered to wrap them but Sadie held them tight in both hands, directly under her chin, willing the smells to penetrate – even a sneeze would be something. Water dribbled down her coat.

If only Graham hadn't laughed. Grey eyes creasing and the snarl of his crooked mouth. All she could think about was that leather jacket of his. The rancid odour of animal skin. She had never considered leather until Graham had become for-ever associated with it. It was the flesh on his back, she had never seen him with it off. It was roughing up and bobbling grey in places, elbows and around the collar. It stank.

Now flowers rotted in the flat. The water in five different vases turning brown and green. Thick residual vegetation clung to some. Sadie could see this through the clear glass of three of them. Each contained roses that had become dry and skeletal. Their flowers had turned to paper. Beautiful paper roses like she used to make for Mum.

The two opaque vases, both blue, a set, hid the stained water but the sunflowers had drooped and verdigris crept up the stems. The heads had shrivelled and been sucked inwards, necks broken. But the petals were still strangely yellow.

'Usual, Graham?'

He nodded. Elbows propped on the bar, hands clasped in front of him. She started to pour him his pint of heavy, tipping the glass and letting the brown liquid filter down one side.

'So, what's this I'm hearing about you goin' off?'

'Aye, back up north for a while.'

She sat the pint in front of him and waited as ritual intended for him to tell whatever story it was until he proffered the £1.90.

'What for? We not good enough here for you, I suppose?'

He was staring at her. Too intensely for polite conversation. The other barflies, Tam and Willy, wee toothless George and Dougie who had played football for Thistle years ago, they didn't speak to her like this. They chatted. Weather, football results, so-and-so is divorced isn't it a shame. But Graham – or Grimey as Sadie and the other girl behind the bar, Louise, liked to call him – was a different sort of man altogether.

'Where is it you're heading?'

'Inverness.'

Sadie was careful not to move too closely over the bar as Grimey had a tendency to grab your wrist and yank you towards him. Leather stinking and the staleness of rollies and booze and the hovering base note of unwashedness. Grime.

'Driving?'

'Yeah.'

'Last time my pal went up there he was driving up that A9, is it?'

She nodded.

'He came across an accident. A car driven off the road, the bonnet on fire. He gets out his car and runs to the guy's windae. He's struggling with his seatbelt, you know. So Jimmy gets him to roll doon his windae and says, "What happened?" and the guy says, "Some fucker's run me off the road but I cannae get ma seatbelt aff." So Jimmy's reaching in through the windae tuggin' at this guy's belt and he's right, it's totally stuck. So he says, "Hang tight, ah've goat the thing that's gonnae get you outta there." So Jimmy runs back tae his car, reaches in the back for his knife, he turns round and the whole car is in flames. And then BOOM! The bloody car explodes. The guy still inside and everything.'

And he laughed. Laughed about fucking luck. And Sadie felt sick again. Her throat thick and tight. She managed to turn her back to him; pretended to stack the short glasses, the voddy glasses.

And Grimey calmed down, coughed his way back down to reality.

'What you going up north for?'

But she opened the hatch to the cellar, rattled down the steep stairs that had the better of almost all the staff. She reached the massive tray of ice that churns up new and plunged both her arms deep into the freezing mass.

The flowers would have to be chucked out, she knew that. But they had become part of the background. Seen but unseen. Another thing to be dealt with.

Knowing what to pack was difficult. Something for the funeral. But how many pairs of pants: how long would she be staying? Probably only until the Sunday. If that, even. Kirsty will be there, she said in her head. Kirsty will be there. Kirsty will be there. A comfort. How long will she stay for? Maybe only for the Thursday. Would Kirsty go back? Back down to James? James might be coming too.

If she made a list it would make things easier. Pen and the envelope from the gas bill. Should she send flowers? *Flowers?* she wrote on the back of the envelope. And then underneath:

black dress
tidy flat
underwear
fill car with petrol
phone Kirsty
phone Mum
tell work
toiletries etc.
go to chemist
charge mobile
switch off heating
pull out plugs
tissues

John Mc Geown

For a Friday morning, District Court number four was unusually busy. One of five cornerstones of justice that lie in a side street disguised from public view, the justice dispensed here unfit for media consumption. Verdicts unquestioned, testimony dismissed, the only certainty disorder.

James Geraghty sat on one of the long wooden benches in the hall outside. He had been waiting since nine thirty, when for once, given that Winterburn was presiding, proceedings had started on time.

– This case. What am I doing with this fucking case? This is NOT my fucking job. Some higher power decrees there be a crackdown on repeat offenders, and so I sit here outside the *district* court, waiting. –

Geraghty's case, Les Clarke, was in the corner with his solicitor and a gang of mates he had mustered up for support. He would be better off without them, Geraghty knew. He tried to look at the file again, but any movement of his head this morning would be dangerous. This morning's hangover meant even a slight shift could set off the sirens attached to the nerve endings across his frontal lobe. If one sounded, the rest would follow.

He raised the file to eye level, but now the blood wasn't flowing to his hands. He was out of options.

The tall oak door of the courtroom swung open, sparing Geraghty the agony of decision. It burst against the wall and he moaned as the fragile peace inside his head was shattered. The sirens began to crash into one another, howling inside his skull. The sun that cut through the open door hurt his eyes. Was there no let-up?

Someone was hovering beside him. He decided to look up; it could get no worse. A court official stood with a disapproving look on his face.

'Mr Geraghty, your case will be called shortly.'

He sighed, too exhausted to care. The official turned on his heel, unimpressed. Geraghty gave no thought to it, turning to the Red Bull in his bag. He would have to get to it somehow. He could not simply lunge down and grab it, that would be too risky.

Cautiously, he pulled at the bag with his foot, then slid his arms out, trying not to move the sirens. It was no use. He dove down and fished out the can. On mornings like this, already beyond the medical community's recommended dosage of Solpadeine, Geraghty knew his remaining hope lay with the can of Red Bull. If it did not give him a temporary boost to perform, to pass as normal, nothing would.

The case would be called any minute. He stood up uncomfortably and downed the drink. Something like adrenaline began to kick in, the sirens faded. Five minutes, he thought. That's all it'll take.

– Then stop off for a quick one on the way back! –

Just to keep the motor running. To get over the worst of it. He pulled his shoulders back and painfully raised his head, chin jutting out, and walked into the courtroom, brown blazer slung over one shoulder, bag on the other.

At a distance, the official eyed him again. Same old shit, Geraghty thought, and stood off to one side. At each end of the room two large wooden partitions rose up, barricades dividing the state from its subjects. At the front, the first barrier sheltered the court officials, reporters, the judge. Sandwiched between the two ramparts were the solicitors, Gardai, probation officers, and whoever was on parade in the name of justice.

At the back were thirty or so feeble creatures: the junkies, the drunk, the disorderly, the unfortunates, or the just plain stupid. Clarke fell firmly in with the latter. Geraghty looked down to the file again. This was the third occasion in the last two years when Mr Clarke had been caught urinating on his neighbours' property. The first two occasions, he had chosen the front garden, and night, to veil the undertaking. This time he had arrived back from the local after a Liverpool game on a Saturday afternoon and taken a piss through the letter-box. Geraghty smiled slyly and looked over to Clarke as he scanned the description of the family terrier's reaction to his behaviour.

He'd been hospitalised for only a few days, but now had to account for himself yet again in court. Geraghty flicked through the rest of the file. All he discovered was that Clarke had initiated a civil suit for damages as a result of the terrier's actions and the ensuing psychological trauma.

The case was called. Geraghty made it to the lectern safely, propping himself up against it with his elbows. Clarke rolled up, all arms and hips, swagger oozing out of the red tracksuit. White trainers pumped, baseball cap tilted perfectly to the right, bling-heavy necklaces draped over a pale hairless chest.

Winterburn gazed down from the bench, distinctly unimpressed. His long grey hair swept back from a strong widow's peak, brushing down to the robes that flowed outward on to the bench.

'Mr Clarke, how good of you to grace us with your presence this morning.'

Geraghty had to suppress a smile. It could not be risked with the sirens. The rest of the courtroom felt no such need. The few Gardai and lawyers milling around behind Geraghty knew what was coming.

'Ahh, no problem, yur hona.'

'This is your third visit to us here?'

'Yea.'

'And you do, of course, realise the gravity of the situation?'

'I do a cours, yur hona, an I'm very sorry for takin up tha' court's tiam.'

'Believe me, Mr Clarke, you are not wasting our time. It is our duty to deal with an offence such as this. Justice is not to be apologised for.'

Clarke's solicitor glared at him. He had probably been warned to keep his mouth shut, Geraghty mused. Best option.

'Well then, how does your client plead, Ms Mc Causland?'

'Guilty, your honour.'

'Very good,' said Winterburn, and a collective snigger passed through the back of the courtroom. He looked up and it immediately died off. They would be next.

'Mr Geraghty, would you like to proceed?'

'Yes, Judge.' Geraghty had just caught the smell of alcohol, and was paranoid it was emanating from him.

– It could be Clarke! Of course! Even if Winterburn caught it all the way up at the bench he would just assume it was Clarke anyway!–

Encouraged, he composed himself, and launched into the doctrine handed down by his superiors. No need for facts here. The words rolled off his tongue.

'Career defendant . . . previous convictions . . . slap on the wrist not enough . . . finds his actions amusing . . . no sign of remorse . . .'

Minutes passed. Geraghty glanced over to see Clarke grinning. Winterburn did not spot it. The temper rumbled.

– How dare he? Laugh at me, here, laugh at the court?–

The words stopped floating through his mind, started to flash instead.

'Serious offence . . . lucky to be charged with trespass . . . breaking and entering . . . getting off lightly.'

The look on Clarke's face changed: grin dropping to a frown, then a grimace. Geraghty could feel him staring over at him. He pushed on, the temper unrestrained now, an edge to his voice.

'State wants the maximum punishment . . . society demands it . . .'

The rest of the room was paying attention now. The solicitors in the middle stared – what the fuck is he doing getting all worked up over this shit, a routine case? The Gardai tensed, sensing trouble. Even Winterburn, staring down at the case file on the bench, started to notice Geraghty's tone. He looked up, surprised. Geraghty ploughed on.

'Your honour, the prosecution believes the maximum six-month sentence for public indecency to be absolutely necessary in this case.'

Clarke's neck bulged and turned red.

'The prosecution feels, your honour, that the state must make clear its stance on the matter as did the family dog.'

The courtroom exploded in laughter, Winterburn's gavel smashed down, and Clarke launched himself across the room into Geraghty's frame. They went down together, Geraghty hitting the ground first, jewellery splayed across his face, a tangle of red and brown, rolling around in the dust. Before the Gardai could pull Clarke off his fist crashed into Geraghty's cheek.

The room was in uproar, Winterburn's gavel banged down repeatedly.

'Order! Order! Order!'

Clarke's mates jeered in the background, 'Go'an, Lesbo!'

His solicitor shook her head in disbelief. Clarke was handcuffed and dragged out shouting, 'Ya fuckin' wanker! I'll kill ya!'

Clarke's solicitor helped Geraghty up. Things were not good. He faltered; she steadied him; he fell over again, nearly taking her with him. More laughter from the back gallery.

Winterburn's gavel again. Small explosions were detonating inside his head. Someone brought over a chair and Geraghty struggled up to sit in it. He could see the face of Clarke's solicitor hovering over him before he blacked out.

A half-hour later he came to, with the silhouette of a bloated paramedic standing over him.

– Pinned to the floor – the embarrassment! –

He knew the slightest movement would shift the sirens.

– But I have to get up! They're all looking at me! –

He decided to risk it, first sitting, kneeling, then slowly standing. A paramedic was at his arm, he shook him off. He moved to walk out.

'Mr Geraghty . . .'

– Winterburn – what the fuck could he want? –

'Will you be pressing charges?'

Geraghty could do no more than half shrug, half nod.

'Well, I hope Mr Clarke enjoys his stay at the taxpayers' expense then. I will gladly take the stand as a witness to ensure he does.'

Laughter rolled across the room again, then the gavel, the fucking gavel. He had to get out of there. After an argument with the paramedic about going to get checked up they let him free. Geraghty began the walk to the river again, and up to O'Connell Street. Straight home. Straight home.

SHADOW AND SUBSTANCE
(extract from a novel in progress)

MAGGIE WALKER

Growing Pains 1982

The first time Danny and I made love, we were lying together on the leather sofa. Miles was playing softly for us and the music ached through my body like a longing. The scent of flowers hung heavy in the air. Dan began very gently to trace over my face with his fingers; when he reached my mouth, he explored the inside of my lips and my teeth and tongue. Then he rolled me on to my back and kissed me, a deep, deep kiss, slow and sweet as poured honey.

'Are you ready, Julie?' he said, looking right in my eyes. I was too full of love to speak, so I just nodded.

Afterwards we lay there for ages, not talking much, just feeling. Of course I said, nearly sobbing, 'I love you, Danny, I love you so much.' He never said it to me, but he kissed me and smiled in my face as though I was the most beautiful thing he had ever seen. And as I lay there, breathing him in, with my cheek resting against his arm, and him stroking my body so tenderly, I knew he did love me. I felt so intensely, so acutely, it seemed like even the air was alive and I knew he must feel it too. I wondered then if you could actually die of love.

He brought me to life, Danny did. This was not having a childish crush or a dream of someone I didn't know at all. It was vividly, dazzlingly real, as though I'd lived my life behind shaded glass until then.

I couldn't get enough of him. I made sure I fixed an alibi with Mum so I could see him whenever he could see me. I told her I was doing loads of extra revision at school and at Sarah's house, and I might be late home sometimes. It never occurred to her I was lying; why would it?

Even though I was in a fever of love most of the time, I was still bothered by the gaps in his life I couldn't fill. We never had regular times when we met. Sometimes he'd be there after school and sometimes he wouldn't. I never saw him at the weekends. He showed me all the rooms in the flat but we never sat anywhere except the white sitting room. Every time we made love it was in there, on the sofa or the carpet, never in his enormous bed with the white fur cover. Each time I left him, he'd say: 'See you then, Julie Adams.' But he never made arrangements to see me again. Whereas, for that brief time, my thoughts were almost completely obsessed by him, it seemed he had a life that ran quite separately from me. That made me miserable sometimes when we were apart, but I was always so ecstatic when we were together, I'd forget.

It lasted for almost seven weeks – until 25 February to be exact – the day I had lessons cancelled in the afternoon. It was one of those glorious winter days that seduce you into thinking it's spring. The crocuses were a riot of purple and gold along the school drive and the grass was so green it looked as though it had been newly painted. Even old Bert, the groundsman, looked quite sprightly as he pottered round with his wheelbarrow. I had this wonderful, romantic, stupid idea that I would go up to Dan's flat and post through his door the letter I'd sat up half the night before writing to him: *How do I Love Thee?* in three pages of prose.

It took me almost an hour to walk from school, along the side of the river and up the hill. My heart was dancing under a sky as cloudless and sunny as I felt. I took off my hat and let my hair down, too happy to care if a prefect saw me. As I turned the corner of his road, I was humming 'Every Time We Say Goodbye', and then I saw them: my Danny coming out of the house with A Woman. She was a Real Grown-Up Woman, elegant, poised, beautiful, and years older than him. I stood as still as death and watched him kiss her, or rather, I watched her kiss him. It wasn't a kiss like our kisses, mine and Dan's, where I'd spend ages exploring his mouth with my tongue and my lips. It was brief and cool, I doubt if she even smudged her lipstick, but I knew, even *I* knew it was a carnal kiss. I watched him as his eyes followed her to her car. I watched her blow her gloved fingertips to him as she drove away. I watched him pull at his hair as he turned towards the house. And then he saw me.

I turned and ran. I heard him calling after me, 'Julie, Julie, wait,' but I didn't stop. I ran and ran until I couldn't breathe any more and had a violent stitch in my side. When I could go no further, I stood, bent double, panting like a hunted animal, drawing in great raw breaths from the air that had suddenly gone cold. Then I threw up, there, by the side of the road, in one of the poshest streets in Bristol. In a revolting mix of school dinner and school pudding, I threw up my innocence and my belief. If only it had been that easy to get rid of the love.

Somehow I stumbled my way to the bus station, climbed like a zombie on to the bus and got myself home. As I opened the door I thanked God the house was empty. In the bathroom I washed out my mouth and wiped the dribble of sick off my blazer. Then I went downstairs, put Tchaikovsky's *Pathetique* on the record player, because it was the saddest record I had ever heard, and waited for my life to end. I knew no one could feel so much pain and go on living. I didn't cry. I just felt the hurt wash through and through me in great, heaving waves. It wasn't just jealousy, it was bewilderment and grief and shame that I had been such a fool.

There was a knock at the door. I ignored it. It came again and I vaguely wondered if it could be Danny, but I knew he would never come to the house. He would never see me again, that was surely the one thing I had to be grateful for. I was wrong. His voice came calling faintly through the door.

'Julie, if you're in there, you must let me in, I have to talk to you . . . Julie.' I got up like someone in a trance, walked through the hall and opened the door. He was standing halfway along the path, looking up at the windows. When he saw me he came towards me, holding out his hand.

'Julie,' he said. I stood staring at him, waiting for him to tell me what he could never tell me – that I hadn't seen what I saw.

'Julie,' he said again, 'please.' I looked at his outstretched hand. What did he want me to do? Why was he there?

That was when Mum came home. At first she looked startled to see a young man on our doorstep, but it didn't take her long to recognise him.

'Daniel,' she cried, 'how nice to see you again. It's been so long. Come on in, don't stand on the doorstep.'

Dan reorganised his face into a bleak smile.

'Hello, Mrs Adams,' he said. 'It's nice to see you too.'

'You'll have to forgive madam here,' said Mum, 'at the moment all she can think about is her work. Why don't you go and put the kettle on, Julie?'

We all trooped through the hall. Tchaikovsky's mournful chords were still wailing out from the front room. Mum went in and turned the music off.

'That's better,' she said. 'Come through to the back, Daniel.' I went into the kitchen, filled the kettle, lit the gas and set the tray. I could hear their voices in the sitting room.

'Well, you've certainly changed, Daniel,' said Mum. 'Your nan tells me you're doing really well. How nice of you to come and see us, it must be, what, seven years now?'

'Yes,' said Dan, 'it must be about that.'

'I was so sorry about your grandpa,' said Mum. 'He was a good man. We couldn't get to the funeral because we were in Scotland at the time, but I wrote to your nan. I still see her now and again, you know.'

'Yes, she told me, thanks,' said Dan. 'She still misses him though. So do I, but I don't live there any more, I've moved to Bristol.'

'Yes, your nan told me,' said Mum. 'She says you're doing really well and you've got a car and everything.'

'I've been lucky. It's a good job, really,' said Dan, 'and I've got a good boss. I drive him round on his business trips. We've been all over England.'

From the kitchen, I listened in amazement. How could he sit in our house and talk to my mum like nothing had happened, after what had happened? What was he made of?

'You certainly have changed, Daniel,' Mum repeated. 'I suppose you're living a whole new life now. I remember how close you and Julie used to be when you were little.'

'Yes,' said Dan, 'we were.'

I took in the tea tray, set out the cups and poured the tea while Dan was telling Mum more about his job 'in the jewellery trade'. There were lots of opportunities, he said, like he was going to Paris in a couple of weeks to work there for a while.

Paris?

Paris?

I stared at him for so long I poured half his tea in his saucer. While Mum was telling me how clumsy I was and fussing around mopping up the spill, my mind was going into overdrive. He'd never told me he was going to Paris. He'd never told me anything like as much about himself as he told my mum over that cup of tea. I listened to him, mesmerised. He didn't look at me, but I got the feeling he was trying to tell me things.

'It's a great opportunity,' he said, 'and I want to make sure I can look after Nan. I'm all she's got left now.'

'Of course, that's a wonderful chance,' said Mum, 'and did you know that Julie will be off to Durham if she gets her

A-level grades? Life moves on, doesn't it? I'll miss her, though, and I expect your nan will miss you.'

'I haven't told her yet,' said Dan. 'I only found out today.' And the image of That Woman flashed back into my head, and I left the room, as unobtrusively as I could, went to the bathroom and was sick again.

When I came back down, Dan was standing up, ready to leave.

'Come and see the old school with me, Jules?' he said. I gazed blankly at him.

'That's a good idea,' said Mum, 'it's a beautiful afternoon and you could do with some fresh air, young lady, always stuck over your books. You're looking very pale these days. You two run along.' He stared at me like he was willing me to come with him, then turned and walked out of the room.

'Go on,' said Mum, shooing me out, 'it'll be dark soon – and put your coat on.' I took my school mac from the peg in the hall and followed Dan out of the house.

No one was at the school, so we sat on the bench in the playground, our shadows already long and the air chilly. We sat far enough apart so we didn't touch at all. He kept pulling at his hair and rubbing his hands over his face. Sometimes he seemed as if he was going to speak and then he didn't. Neither of us said anything for ages, but in the end I couldn't keep the hurt inside me any more, it burst right out, as if all of me was a wound he'd come back to probe.

'For God's sake, Daniel Black!' I cried. 'What do you want with me? Haven't you made enough of a fool of me without coming here to gloat? Why don't you just go away wherever it is you're going and leave me alone? I hate you. I hate and despise you. Please, please, just go away.' And of course, all the time I was talking my heart was reminding me that him going away was the last thing I wanted. I wanted him to stay here, next to me for ever and ever. I could smell the nearness of him and I wanted to bury myself in that smell.

He sat for a while, shifting his feet and looking everywhere but at me. At last he said, 'Julie – I don't know why I'm here either. I think I just wanted to see you. I couldn't bear that the look I saw on your face might be the last I saw of you. But now I'm here, I don't know what to say to you, because anything I say that could make things better will sound false. It would be false. I'm not going to lie to you, Julie, I lie to everyone else. I just wanted to see you. I wanted to tell you that you are the most beautiful person I have ever known. You always were. You are open, and honest and passionate and loving and I've learned more from you in these last weeks than in the rest of my life put together. As for going away, well that's OK because I am going away. I'll be leaving for Paris within the month.'

I hated myself for asking, but I asked anyway, although it came out in no more than a whisper: 'Will she be going with you?'

After a pause that seemed to last an hour, he said, 'Yes.'

He stood up and took his keys from his pocket.

'Say goodbye to your mum for me,' he said. 'Be happy, Julie.'

I sat there in the playground as he drove off. I sat there until it got too dark to see clearly and I was frozen to the bone. Maybe I was trying to freeze the pain out of me. Above the school the moon rose, a thin gash in the blackness, close by hung just one star. Over in the church the choir began their practice, 'Jesu, Joy of Man's Desiring', but the sounds held no comfort for me and the words held no meaning. I stared at the empty tarmac. Through the tears that were pouring down my face, I saw two small ghosts, Danny and me playing and growing up together in the school, in the days when happiness was possible. I could hear our laughter, faint and tinny. 'Catch me, catch me,' he called after me, 'come on, Julie, come on.' Then I heard Mum calling me in for tea and the two tiny figures faded away for ever.

'Would Danny like to stay?' she said. 'There's enough for three.'

No More Mulberries
(extract from a novel in progress)

Mary Smith

[Set in Afghanistan. Here Miriam, the British wife of Iqbal, an Afghan doctor, has come to work as an interpreter at a medical teaching camp for Afghan paramedical staff.]

Miriam felt she'd only been asleep for moments when Chaman shook her awake next morning. 'Miriam-jan, it's time for *fajr*. It'll soon be sunrise. Come on, stir yourself.' Miriam groaned, pulling the blanket over her face, but Chaman was insistent. 'We didn't pray last night. Up you get. There's water in the bathroom next door.' Miriam shivered in the chilly morning air as she emerged from her cosy nest.

'We'll have to get to bed a bit earlier tonight,' she said, yawning her way to the bathroom to wash and prepare for prayer. 'I'm too old to be able to sit up half the night talking if I'm to function properly next day.' It had been good, though, she thought, remembering how easy they'd found it to talk, sharing personal stories.

Miriam had spoken a little about Iqbal's reluctance to let her come to the camp, and of how much he seemed to have changed since returning to Afghanistan from Pakistan. Chaman had brought her up to date with what had happened when Ali decided to take a second wife.

'I was devastated,' she'd said. 'I arrived late in the afternoon and the staff at the clinic all came to welcome me back. No one said anything and Ali behaved just as you'd expect a man to behave when his wife comes home after a long holiday.' She grinned at Miriam. 'So everything was fine, very loving, and the girls were pleased to be back with their daddy. Then, next morning as he was leaving for the clinic – as if it was something he'd just remembered, you know, like, "Oh, by the way the cat had kittens while you were away." Only it was, "By the way, I should mention I got engaged last week." '

Chaman had told Miriam that at first she'd thought it was a stupid joke but a friend in the village had, with huge embarrassment and sympathy, confirmed that it was true. 'I could hardly believe it,' she'd continued, 'and although I asked why a thousand times, Ali couldn't give me one good reason for doing it. It was as if he'd had some kind of brainstorm or something. He said he loved me, said he was happy with me, loved our children and had no complaints about me. He kept telling me he was sorry he'd hurt me but when I asked if he would break off the engagement he refused, said he couldn't.'

'But why not? Why couldn't he?' Miriam had been angry on her friend's behalf. 'It's an outrageous way to behave, and totally against what Islam teaches.'

Chaman had shrugged. 'Oh, he knew all that. Miriam, some nights he cried, actually cried about the mess he had got himself into but he would not break off the engagement because he would lose face. He was convinced that everyone would say the girl's family had changed their mind because he was a leprosy patient. He thought no one would believe that he was the one who wanted to break it off.'

'This loss of face business is something I really struggle to understand,' Miriam had said quietly, thinking about how often she had heard Iqbal use the same justification. 'Would people really think it was because of the leprosy? The family must have known about it when they agreed to the engagement, surely. Why would that be the issue if he broke it off?'

'Ali would believe he'd lost face,' Chaman had said. 'If someone feels it, then it becomes the truth. Anyway, life was horrible. In the evenings after work he would go to see her, instead of spending time with his daughters. It's strange . . . I wasn't really jealous of Fatima. I think I was too angry to feel any jealousy. He'd paid two and a half hundred thousand Afghanis – money I had earned working for Hansease. I was furious.' She'd shifted into a more comfortable position on her mattress, pulling the blanket round her knees. 'Talking's thirsty work. I could do with some tea.'

Miriam had stood up, pulling her chaddar over her head. 'We could raid the kitchen.' She'd glanced at Ruckshana and Chaman's girls, sound asleep. 'They won't wake up – come on, let's go.' The feeling that they were doing something childishly naughty had made the women giggle as they'd crept from their room and across the compound towards the kitchen. The cook had left out thermoses of boiling water so that he could quickly reboil it for the morning tea – Chaman had added a pinch of tea leaves to the smallest one while Miriam had found the glasses and sweets. Back in the room, glass of tea in hand, she'd settled against a pillow to hear the rest of her friend's story. 'Did you know the girl – this Fatima?'

'Of course, everyone knows everyone – must be the same in Sang-i-Sia.' As Miriam had nodded in agreement, Chaman had continued, 'It was worse than that, she was my friend. Well, I'd always thought she was. We spent a lot of time together and she used to look after Feroza when I was busy in the clinic. I even went to her house, to try to talk her into breaking off the engagement, but she refused to see me. Although Ali wouldn't admit it, I suspect part of it was that he desperately wants a boy – and I'd produced two girls by then. I know,' she'd continued as Miriam had opened her mouth to protest, 'I know and Ali knows very well that it's the father who determines the sex of a child. Goodness knows we've had to explain to people in the clinic often enough but I still have a sneaking suspicion that was one of his reasons.' Chaman had talked of how increasingly depressed Ali had become as the date for the wedding had come ever closer. Chaman had thought about leaving him and returning to Pakistan with the children but there was no way she could make the journey alone and there was no one to whom she could turn for help in making travel arrangements. Also, with winter closing in the roads would soon be closed by snow. A few days before the wedding Chaman had told Ali that she would never accept his new wife in their home, that he must go instead to his in-laws' house and not come home again to her and their children.

'He was really upset. Said he couldn't live without me. Why was I killing him in this way? He felt as though I had thrust a dagger in his heart. You know the sort of thing.' Miriam had nodded. Although she'd never experienced this sort of thing personally, for which she was grateful, she had heard enough stories from her friends to be able to visualise Ali's dramatic performance. 'I told him he'd killed me when he refused to break off the engagement.' Ali had still gone ahead with the wedding, moved in with his new wife. Two weeks later he'd begged Chaman to allow him to come home. 'My heart was breaking but I was determined to be strong,' she'd said. 'I stopped working in the main clinic and held consultations in my own room so I wouldn't have to see him every day. He used to slip little notes under my door, asking me to talk to him.'

'Did you really want him back after what he'd done?' Miriam had been amazed.

'I love him,' Chaman had replied simply, adding, 'and despite what he did I knew he never stopped loving me. We had a strong marriage before all of this – oh, we had fights and difficult times, of course – and I didn't really want to live without him. Eventually I agreed to meet him and we talked. He was a mess. He knew he'd made a huge mistake. In going ahead with the marriage he had actually lost face more than if he had ended the engagement. The people in the villages from round about were all on my side – not only the women, but their husbands too, thought he had behaved very badly. He couldn't bear to be with Fatima and she, poor girl, knew very well that he didn't want to stay with her. Finally it was she who brought things to a conclusion by telling Ali that she wanted a divorce – wanted it so much that she, or at least her family, were willing to pay back most of the bride price. So, I got my husband back, although it took a long time for us to get back to where we were before he became engaged to Fatima.'

Miriam had been pleased that her friend's marriage had survived such a traumatic event but she'd felt that it wasn't quite the happy-ever-after ending for everyone that Chaman was implying. She'd shifted uncomfortably on her mattress, not sure how to say what was on her mind. Chaman, yawning, had been gathering their empty glasses and thermos. Finally Miriam had said, 'But although it was the end of the problem for you and Ali, didn't it leave Fatima's life in ruins? How would she find another husband with everyone knowing what had happened?'

Chaman had shrugged. 'She should've thought of that before trying to steal my husband,' she'd said coolly. 'She has married since – has a little girl now. Her father owns a lot of land and she has no brothers so it wasn't too difficult for her family to find someone else. But you are right, what Ali did would have destroyed the marriage prospects of a girl in different circumstances. Knowing that my husband was so careless of the happiness of so many people is not easy to live with.' She had begun to rearrange her bedding, adding, 'It's been tough but I do believe he's truly sorry and we have to try to build on that. Now, unless we want to get a severe telling-off from Dr Jeanine for being late on our first morning, I think we should sleep.'

Now, recalling their conversation, as the icy water on her face chased away her sleepiness, Miriam was glad to be sharing a room with Chaman rather than Jeanine. At the thought of the boss she hurriedly left the bathroom, returning to their room to pray before waking the children. By the time they reached the staff room most of the paramedics, looking as though they had spent half the night playing cards, were already seated on the floor around a long *dustakhan* on which Moh'd Amir the cook had set bowls of hard-boiled eggs and piles of nan. The three foreign doctors came in just behind Miriam, Chaman and the children. 'No Jeanine?' Miriam asked Anwar, who was pouring tea over several heaped teaspoons of sugar in his glass. 'I didn't think she'd be late.'

'She's having breakfast before she comes over,' he replied. Almost immediately there came the sound of a jeep approaching. 'That'll be her now. No chance the *rais* would be late.' It was as if someone had pulled a switch, shocking the men into sudden action, and Miriam watched in amusement as they swallowed the last mouthfuls of breakfast, gulping tea as they grabbed notebooks and checked pens were in their pockets, before rushing off to the room set aside for the lectures.

'She has quite an electrifying effect, doesn't she?' Dr Eva also looked amused at the speed with which Jeanine's arrival had everyone leaping to their feet. 'Shall we get started?' Dr Anwar led them to a room furnished with a small table, a couple of folding metal chairs and an examining table. Eva nodded approvingly. 'Good, I'm glad it's a decent size. In the last place I worked in what I'm sure was a cupboard.'

There was already a queue of women outside the room, each clutching a small square of cardboard as though it was a talisman. As Anwar, after checking there was nothing else required, bowed his way out of the room, half a dozen women pushed their way in. Chaman pushed them back out, explaining to the women as she did so that each would be seen in turn according to the numbers on the cardboard squares. As none of the women could read the number on her card, and each insisted she'd arrived before the others, it took several minutes for Chaman to sort the group into order. The first patient came in triumphantly waving her number at Eva, and sat down looking expectantly from Miriam to Eva.

JOHN
(extract from a novel in progress)

FELIX BOON

The moment that life begins.

It's supposed to be something special, bordering on the divine, like in those Open University programmes with the 1980s synth music in the background. It should be two people in love, everything warm and soft focus, making a baby the natural way. It's not supposed to be thwacking off into a plastic beaker to pictures of a fat bird called Karen. Still, a lot of life is about compromise and you have to take what you can get. I got the beaker.

And my beaker was tiny. Hardly much bigger than those little pots of jam you get in hotels. I prayed to God I didn't miss. I tried not to think about it. I hadn't slept the night before and my nerves were jangling as it was. As the nurse went through the rules I nodded slowly, barely taking it all in. The lack of sleep had done funny things with my brain: most of it felt like it had been stamped on and the tiny part left over was fizzing away like an aspirin. A memory of a school experiment. Lumps of potassium and caesium fizzing away on contact with water. Done behind safety glass. The bowl exploded with the caesium. My head was going to explode. Oh God, I thought, I've lost the ability to edit. I'm literally thinking every thought.

I closed the door behind me and took a look around at the room they'd given me to do the job in. It was cramped and ball-achingly bland. There was a cloying stench of pine-scented air freshener. The carpet was a hideous pastel colour and the walls an infected shade of beige. Someone had attempted to cover them up with several large photographic prints of mountain ranges. Fuck knows why. Perhaps they thought that sort of thing helped? There was a sink – I had to wash my hands, I remembered that. There were a couple of comfy chairs, and perched on a small coffee table between them, just in front of a dusty yucca plant, there was a stack of ancient *Bella* and *OK!* magazines. In any circumstances, it was not the best place to have a wank.

I was there because my wife Jane and I were unable to make a baby the natural way. It was painfully simple. All I had to do was knock out my teaspoon's worth of DNA and let them get on with it. In truth, I was supposed to have done this already at home that morning, except I was so stressed, trying to organise Jane, booking the taxi and everything else, that I forgot where I'd put the beaker. After a lot of humming and hawing, the clinic said I could do it there. But they could only give me fifteen minutes, otherwise we'd have to reschedule the appointment. Needless to say, given the mood that Jane was now in, I was on my own. With everybody waiting for me outside.

I went over to the sink and gave my hands a quick scrub. Nearby there was an ageing Samsung TV and a clunky-looking Sony VCR that made Betamax look high-concept. The TV remote was the same size as a small child. Stuffed in the cubbyhole below it there were a couple of porn mags. Even though I was wanking to a deadline, I couldn't help feeling a bit disappointed. There was nothing classy, just fading jizz rags full of fat, surly, menopausal heifers with heavy milky-white tits. These nurses really didn't have the first fucking clue. I pressed eject on the VCR. There was a pause, like it had forgotten what that did. Finally, after clicking and shuddering, a copy of *Dirty Housewives Volume 6* emerged. They were rude and nasty, apparently.

My mind had started to frame the scene up as a feature. Normally, I wouldn't write about this kind of thing – I made my living reviewing hi-fis and audio equipment – but a few years back I'd managed to get some work experience with *Loaded* and, although it didn't work out, they still took the odd thing from me here and there. I figured this would make quite a nice little filler. 'How Good is NHS Porn? A Wanker's Guide'. If I hadn't been trying to make a baby then I would have started taking notes. I played around with NHS and IVF, trying to think up some other titles. National Jaffa Service and National Hard-on Service were the best I could manage. I could rate it from one to five on a knuckle-shuffle scale . . . Time to get going. I closed my eyes and looked up at the ceiling.

'To my as yet unborn child, please forgive me.'

On went the film. And *Jesus!* it was bad. One of them looked like Judith Chalmers. I gave it two soul-crushing minutes then turned it off. With a sinking heart I turned my attention to the magazines, pulling out a couple at random. The first was a nudist magazine, full of fat middle-aged men with shrivelled cocks and sandals. This place was definitely becoming a one-knuckle wank. I switched mags. And so to Karen. *Readers' Wives*. She had blond hair, dark eyebrows and dark bags under her eyes. To be honest, Jacqui looked like a crack-whore. She had pushed her huge breasts together and her hands had almost disappeared beneath the two mounds of veiny white flesh. Every page was all about her fucking ginormous fun-bags – big tits weren't my thing. I flicked forward. The next girl was a nurse called Mandy. I did a mock salute and took out my penis.

Nothing happened. My cock was about the size of a cocktail sausage. I just stood there, shaking away, looking at the ads for sexual health. Thinking about what we needed to get from the shops on the way home. Anything other than think about why I was actually there.

When I thought things couldn't get worse, my phone rang. The caller display said DICKHEAD – my best mate Alex. I stuffed the phone back in my jeans and waited for it to ring out, which, after two full polyphonic renditions of the *Bond* theme, it did. He rang back. 'Ah fuck off,' I said, turning the phone off.

I'd been avoiding Alex a lot recently. In fact, this time around, Jane and I had been avoiding pretty much everybody. The last time we'd tried IVF I'd made the mistake of telling people about it – something Jane will never let me forget. Yes, of course, with 20:20 hindsight, I could see that maybe it hadn't been a good idea, but how was I supposed to know? The problem is, the moment they find out, your friends suddenly become a complete nightmare. They phone constantly and start 'popping round' for cups of tea, fishing for the latest piece of news, which more often than not you don't want to tell them. Our home became this weird sort of drop-in centre for gossip junkies. They never worked out how much it all upset us, Jane especially. So this time, nobody knew.

I stared at the battered magazine and turned another page, willing myself to get an erection. Mandy was now naked, her arse to camera and, judging by her over-the-shoulder grimace, she was really fucking bored. There was a bedpan beside her and I found myself wondering where porn people get their props from. Was there a shop? Did the NHS help out with that sort of thing? Surely not. However, nurses are stock porn favourites. They're never going to go away. It seemed perfectly plausible that the NHS did loan stuff out. Maybe there was a series of possible tax breaks in place? When I thought about it, it all had an eerie ring of a government cost-cutting initiative.

I looked at my watch. It took a moment for my scrambling brain to remember that, in an attempt to make the day seem like a bit of fun, I'd worn the Disney watch. The display was hidden by a Mickey Mouse face that you had to lift up to see the time. This hadn't gone down well with Jane either. Now, with all the weight of what I was supposed to be doing on my shoulders, I felt like a bit of a twat.

According to Mickey, I had been in the booth for eight minutes already. Eight minutes? Where had it all gone? I could just see Jane and God knows how many doctors waiting for me in the corridor outside, tutting and getting *really* pissed off.

I was buzzing with the possibility of failure. If I didn't finish soon we'd miss our slot. It could take weeks – months
even – to get another appointment. I tried to make myself get
into it but it was all too weird, and I stopped again. Everyone
outside knew I was having a wank. Worse, they wanted me to
finish up quickly. It was adding to my headache and making
me confused. A part of me – the part that had carefully assim-
ilated every shagging tip and technique *FHM* ('always listen
to the lesbians') and *Cosmo* had ever published – was howling
in a sexually bewildered man-rage. Feeling desperate, I tried
coaxing myself along by imagining the rewards of fatherhood
– this was Goal-Centred Masturbation. Just think how good
it'll be, I told myself. Just think how good it'll be to be a dad.
That's the reward. A Father. THE PATRIARCH! A cool
dad. The kind of dad you could speak to about anything.
A nice dad . . .

It occurred to me then that my entire idea of parenthood
was just a reaction against my own father; me trying to put
things right with the next generation. Suddenly it was all I
could think about. I closed the magazine quickly, wary of
forging some unconscious link between my father and bad
porn. In the last twelve months I'd become obsessed with the
way my parents had brought me up, so these were hardly new
fears. I hadn't really looked at the IVF blogs but I reckoned
the fear of repeating past mistakes must be one of the biggies.
My father and I weren't really on speaking terms, so I had no
idea what he thought of the IVF. Mum said she had told him
all about it, despite me asking her not to. Spiteful old bastard.
I bet he never said a word about it, even to her. Who could

say what our parents have passed on to us? It's not just DNA. It all boiled down to one thing: what if I become like my father?

I could not let it happen.

I let out a sigh and ran a hand through my hair, twiddling at one of the thick curls. I stared at a photo of a mountaineer, standing on a snow-covered summit and taking in the view. Apart from being one of the most stressful moments of my life it was unbelievably *boring*. I want Jane, I thought, taking off my glasses and rubbing at my aching eyes. Tarzan want Jane. Make wank-wank go quick-quick. Sliding the glasses back on, I beat my fists against my chest and let out a restrained wail. The quiet that followed seemed to mock me.

Just then the thought of everyone waiting for me outside yanked me back into real time. I flipped back Mickey's face and checked the time again. Twelve minutes. Twelve fucking minutes! Fuck. The thought of being sent home made my stomach squeeze together like a clenched fist. I couldn't not do this. After everything, I couldn't fuck this up. I couldn't. I urged myself on and started pumping away again. Nothing. *Come on*, I told myself, feeling almost like crying. Even more nothing. I was starting to lose my temper. This incredible sense of injustice about it all welled up inside me.

'This is f-f-f-ucking . . . *ridiculous. Fucking stupid!*' I hissed, stamping my feet.

It was becoming hopeless and getting worse. Ever since our decision to go with IVF I'd felt a guilty sense of dissatis-faction with the whole business and now the feeling was back with a vengeance, bringing me to another grinding halt. I felt cheated by IVF. It was robbing me of something fundamental – apart from killing things, the most instinctive, primal function of every man is to inseminate. It's like they say about women who give birth by Caesarean: they feel like they're missing out. I'd tried not to dwell on it and, given our complete lack of alternatives, this was the most ridiculous *quibble* but I couldn't help it. I tried shaking it off by pretending I would tell the child they had been conceived to mountain views but, all in all, it seemed a pretty piss-poor consolation just then.

I kept seeing them all waiting for me. I'd blown any last chance of coming out of this with even a shred of dignity about ten minutes ago. I could just see the looks on their faces when I came out. They'd all think I got off on this shit and had gone back for seconds. I just had to get it over and done with. Finish up. Quick.

I went back to the porn stash, looking for something – anything – that would get me focused. I found phone ads. Lots of tiddly pictures and short hard words.

Call Me . . . . . . I'm waiting	Hot Lesbian Action!!!!	Wet 'n' ready!!!!	Triple XXX Action!!!!!	Will make you cum in under a minute!!!!
0898 666552	0898 666414	0898 666444	0898 696969	

Under a minute . . .? Please, GOD, let it be true. I checked the time again. Nothing wrong with a bit of dirty talk, I told myself, pulling out my phone and turning it back on. I'd only keyed in a couple of numbers when my phone went off. 'Ride of the Valkyries' – it was Jane.

'What?'

'What's happening?' She sounded edgy.

'Not a lot . . .'

'How long are you going to be?'

'Fuck's sake – I don't know! As long as it takes.'

'We haven't got that long. You've been ages . . .'

'Listen, this isn't helping. I can really do without this just now.' There was a moment's silence at the other end, like she was thinking things over. She sighed.

'Listen,' she said, softer now. 'John, don't worry about it. We can come back an . . .'

'I am not coming back. I want to start this now. I can't . . . we have to do this. Just . . . I'll do it, just give me a minute.'

'You're sure?'

'Yes.'

'OK, then. Hurry up!'

'Don't tell me to . . .' She giggled and then rang off. '*Je-sus!*' I looked at the porn mags.

'Ahh, *fuckkk's* sake . . . I don't feel like it now.' I couldn't do phone sex so soon after speaking to Jane. It was . . . confusing. And what if she tried ringing back and the phone was engaged? How do you explain that? Who else do you speak to while masturbating?

And then, as if to answer, my phone went off again.

'*Fuuuuuuuucckkkkkkkkkk!*'

I thought it would be Jane, chivvying me along, but no, it was my mother. Of course. I turned the fucking thing off, shooting a look at the ceiling. Someone upstairs was taking the piss. Right, I told myself, you are not going to fuck this up. I squeezed my eyes shut and tried to think about nothing. Pitch black. Absolutely nothing.

By some margin, this was the worst wank I'd ever had.

Eventually, I managed to bring up my teaspoon's worth, the moment taking me almost by surprise. I even managed to get most of it in the beaker. After a moment I felt it warm to body temperature and I stuck it in the drop-off tray, glad to be rid of it. I walked back through to the waiting area, feeling both relief and excitement wash through me, and with the sense that I had achieved something bloody marvellous. We were back on track.

Watching the Sky
(extract from a novel in progress)

Alison Irvine

They were lucky with the day and the sharpness of the sky and the glare of the low sun behind the clouds. Faye showed Lewis the footbridge where they admired the straightness of the main road and the shapes of buildings. Lewis pointed south and told her his building sites were beyond the tower blocks. When they reached the open land by the waterworks Faye let Annie's dog off the lead and they watched it sniff and follow birds. Faye thought of Annie, quiet in her flat, tending her sore bones. She showed Lewis young oaks, grown from acorns that had survived one winter. Their stems were delicate and the leaves wide and crisp. She held her arm against the dog's front paws to stop it treading on the young shoots.

As they were close to the ground it was easy to roll on to the hard, dry earth and press against the length of each other, to hear the creak of their jackets and the scuffing of their jeans. She meant it to be physical and she meant for them to let their breath out hard and keep close and be warmed by each other. Lewis tucked his fingers under the waist of her jeans, dogs barked somewhere far off and they sat up with their hands on their knees, the white sky hanging unchanged and the dog running in circles around itself.

Traffic sped along the road that cut through the open land. Faye picked crushed leaves from the elbows of her jacket.

'You don't look as if you'd like all this earth and mud and leaves,' Lewis said. He pulled train tickets from his jacket pocket, shuffled them and put them back.

'Oh but I do,' Faye said. And she did. 'Can you hear the cars on the cattle grid?'

They listened to the rub of wheels on the grid. 'Cows used to graze here,' she said.

'Is this London?' Lewis said and Faye didn't answer because she presumed it was a question that wasn't meant to be answered.

'What do you like?' she said.

'The sea. The river. Fried eggs.'

'Do you like this, where we are?'

'I do.'

But Lewis's clothes had the feel of the inside about them. His jacket held the scent of smoke, his jeans were dark, his trainers clean. And his eyes looked like they held on to things they'd seen for a long time.

They walked along a path which led to a pond by the road and a pub and a stone church. There was forest on each side of the road.

'That's where I sit sometimes,' Faye said, and she pointed to a wooden bench by the pond. A woman was sitting on the bench, facing the road with her back to Faye and Lewis. Faye picked up a piece of branch. She watched Lewis kick a stone. Geese flew in a V overhead. She felt suddenly awake and liked the feeling. She whistled and the dog came to her. She held the branch in the air and the dog jumped and yelped. She threw the branch and the dog ran after it. Faye saw the dog's teeth and gums and tongue, its mouth wide as if it was smiling. Faye turned to Lewis and he was stood still, looking at her. He held a stem of wild grass in his hands and watched her. She felt, in that moment, that her life was easy.

When she spoke to Lewis, Faye's voice became light as if run through with soft rain. She spoke gently, her words brimming with the idea of him.

A lorry drove over the cattle grid. Faye watched it pass along the road and noticed the yellow sign on the other side of the pond. She held Lewis's hand and they walked around the pond towards the sign. It had a rusted frame. It said SERIOUS ASSAULT and appealed for witnesses who might have seen something in the middle of the night. Faye touched the black letters on the sign and it occurred to her that police used the signs again and again and changed the letters for each crime. There were fragments of blue and white police tape on the grass. The earth was trampled and dry.

'Let's go home,' she said. They passed the woman on the bench who sat with her hands clasped and raised to her mouth. When Faye looked back to whistle for the dog, she saw that the woman had left the bench and was walking the other way along the path.

On the main road to Faye's flat, street lights were lit and seemed pale against the darkening sky. The door to the pub was open and the heat and smoke and sounds from inside tempted Faye. She kissed Lewis before they went in, the dog waiting by her legs, then Lewis's hands on her hips as she leaned back to look at him. She filled an ashtray with water and put it under the table and they watched the dog drink. It curled itself around its bent legs and laid its head on the carpet.

Lewis drank a pint. Faye drank a vodka. Lewis looked at black and white photographs on the wall: straight-backed men and women standing by market stalls and rowing boats. A woman played a fruit machine, pressing her thumbs gently on the plastic buttons. Next to them, a man folded a newspaper, then sipped from a pint and put the glass on the table. After he had left, Faye took the paper and read the front page. There was a picture of the pond by the church and an article about the attack. Faye and Lewis leaned their elbows on the table and read the details. A runner found the beaten man at seven in the morning. He was breathing, but bones were broken, his head was bleeding, hands and arms and back bruised. He said he remembered nothing more than three youngsters who stuck their hands into his pockets and took coins and cigarettes. And the paper called for relatives or friends to claim the man who survived in critical care, whose clothes were torn, who said he'd no home, who said he slept by the pond.

Lewis said, 'That's why you're an actress, isn't it? To escape this.'

Faye felt agitated. She said, 'I perform because it makes me work hard and I become the best I can be. That's the reason. Not to escape. Nobody escapes what happens anyway.'

'I was only wondering.'

'But you're right. Everyone needs an outlet,' Faye said. 'You see, you – and tell me if I'm wrong – you build your houses and find land and it clips you to the world. It reassures you. Life, projects, homes.'

'I agree with you.' Lewis smiled.

'And the poker?'

'That's where I escape,' he said. 'Same as chess when I was a kid except a bit more rock 'n' roll.'

'And the money you might lose?'

'That's the risk. And you know people need risks.'

He turned the pages of the newspaper and when they came to the back page he flipped the paper over and they looked again at the front page. Faye touched her fingers to the picture.

It was dark when they returned and Annie was standing at her window.

When she opened her front door she said, 'Give me the dog,' and it slipped past her legs, into the kitchen. Faye heard its metal tag tap the side of its food bowl. 'You've no idea,' Annie said. The rims of her eyes were red. 'And who's this?'

Faye said, 'Annie, this is Lewis. Are you feeling any better?'

'You're not to do this again,' she said. 'It was too long and too dark.'

She closed her door. She played her music. Faye and Lewis took off their shoes and trod quietly above her.

★ ★ ★

It was something about the leaves piled on the pavements, loosely touching, stacked softly, with their turning, raging colours, unearthly almost, too beautiful for the speckled grey of the paving stones. And with this sweetness in the city, with the wind kissing the leaves from the trees, Faye and Lewis closed the curtains against the blue sky. Every part of them touched on the sheet on the square bed under the feather quilt. Faye tasted sweat on Lewis's skin and smiled in her head as his fingers pressed and slipped inside her and pulled her mind down through herself to the gentleness of his touch. And that feeling that is like a held note, she clutched it.

They slept in daylight and when they woke, Lewis opened the curtains and they lay in bed watching silver planes cross the sky. Lewis had a painting of the sea on his wall. He had shelves with photographs propped against books. Ties hung on the open door of his wardrobe.

Faye picked up a pencil sharpener from the floor with a Union Jack painted on it.

'That's for my brother, for his travels,' Lewis said.

'Why?'

'Because he might need it.'

'He might need a pencil sharpener?'

'What else could I get him?'

'Sun cream?'

'That's too practical.'

'And a pencil sharpener isn't?'

'It's a gesture.'

Faye said, 'It would be a lovely gesture if you made me a cup of tea.' She returned the pencil sharpener to the floor and stretched her arms wide, one arm falling across Lewis's chest.

'Do you look alike?' she said as she sipped her tea.

'Yeah, we do. But he doesn't have the grey hairs yet.'

Faye put her lips to his hair. 'They suit you, babe.'

'I always think about the differences between us now. When you grow up with only one other you feel incredulous that you came from the same place.'

'Do you get on?' Faye asked.

'Oh yeah. He makes more of an effort than I do. He used to be a bit judgemental about anyone who wasn't like him, used to call me uni-boy, but he went travelling, met his lady, and when he came back he was just the same, but so tolerant. Tolerant and full of compassion. More than I could be. And now he's going away again when we need more of that over here. He's a hippy, in a city kind of way.'

'I hope he stays in love,' Faye said.

'Why do you say that?'

'Because I hate to think of all that compassion wrung out of him just because his heart's fucked up. And I think love has the power to do that. That's its flip side.'

'We were talking about *him*, not love,' said Lewis.

'But I'm just saying, he is the man he is because of love.'

'But even without love he'd be the same man.'

'Or he'd become screwed up and bitter and disappointed,' Faye said.

'That depends on who you are.'

'I'm not saying he'd definitely be like that or I'd be like that . . .'

'But it's possible for other people less opinionated than you?'

'You're not understanding me,' Faye said.

'You're negative.'

'I'm not. I'm realistic.'

'I'm shutting the curtains,' Lewis said. 'It was better that way.'

Later, when his brother Sean arrived, Lewis zipped his jacket and said he wanted to be outside as the day deserved an audience. They sat on the balcony. Sean wore a woollen hat and sipped from a beer bottle. Faye wound a scarf around her neck. She leaned her feet on the balcony railing and watched the sky as the wind blew clouds across it. She wondered if she should leave the brothers alone on the balcony but Lewis kept stroking his fingers on the back of her neck so she stayed.

'Those blokes make me feel like a skiver,' Sean said.

Men were working on the roof of a house. The house was built on land between scrubby gardens. A man climbed a ladder with a piece of turf on his shoulder. He stepped on to the roof, bent his knees and dropped the turf. He climbed down the ladder. Another man picked up the turf and laid it. He worked on his knees. Then the first man returned with another piece of turf. One man wore shorts; another, tracksuit trousers tucked into boots. Below them, a woman walked through rooms. They saw her through glass walls.

'He told me it was an ecological house,' Lewis said. 'That one, laying the turf. Six of them went in on it. All architects, so they designed it themselves.' The man stood up and Lewis waved. The man stood still, staring, and then waved too. 'I hear their radio sometimes.'

'You'll be hearing them sleep-talk soon.'

'I wish we built houses like that,' Lewis said. 'Imagine if everyone got to have a house like that.'

'But glass walls?' his brother said.

'I like that,' Faye said. 'I like seeing what their lives are like.'

'Much the same as ours,' Lewis said.

'Except with a tendency for exhibitionism.'

'Tell me how their grass gets on, will you, if it thrives?' said Sean.

When Lewis went inside to find more beer, Sean said that Lewis had paid for his ticket to Australia. He had given him poker winnings and told him he didn't want the money back.

'It was like picking me up and shaking me and putting me down again,' Sean said. 'I don't know how to thank him.'

'He doesn't seem like he wants thanking,' Faye said. She smiled at Sean. His features were prettier than his brother's. His eyes were alert and he looked out towards the glass house.

'The view over the roofs is lovely,' Faye said.

'Don't muck Lewis about,' said Sean. 'And I know I shouldn't say that.'

Faye was surprised. 'No, you shouldn't,' she said.

'The trouble is, you're as delicate as him and that worries me.'

'Neither of us is delicate,' Faye said.

Lewis came back on to the balcony with bottles of beer. 'Faye's an actress, you know, Sean. She's been on TV but she won't tell me what in. One each for you and one for me,' he said and he handed out the beers.

The Unbelievers
(extract from a novel in progress)

Alastair Sim

[Edinburgh, 1865. Inspector Allerdyce and Sergeant McGillivray, VC are on their way to the castle to interview the brother of the murdered Duke of Dornoch.]

As they crossed the market square a one-legged man emerged, on crutches, from between two stalls. He wore a glengarry from which matted red hair stuck out underneath, a filthy red soldier's jacket with no buttons left and braid that was hanging off by threads, and a kilt so worn and grey you could hardly make out the tartan.

The man held out a tin cup and rattled the coppers in it.

'Spare a few pence for an old soldier, gentlemen, crippled in Her Majesty's service?'

Allerdyce walked by, holding his breath against the stink of filth and whisky and brushing the man's outstretched cup out of his way. He stopped and turned as he heard the sergeant's stern voice:

'Who are you?' he was asking, looking down at the stunted veteran.

'Private James McNeill, if it please.'

'Your regiment?'

'The Ninety-First, Sergeant. Argyll Highlanders.'

'Which company?'

'Captain Ewart's, sir.'

'Stand to attention as you address a senior non-commissioned officer, Private McNeill.'

The veteran attempted to stand straighter, his hands shaking on his crutches.

The sergeant continued: 'Where did you serve?'

'Cape Colony, Mr Sergeant sir, the Crimea, India.'

'Where are your medals?'

'Pawned, Sergeant, to put some thin broth on my table and pay for my poor bed.'

The sergeant's face relaxed slightly.

'Tell me, McNeill, if you were in Mr Ewart's company you must have known Private Aeneas McGillivray of Strath Oykell.'

The veteran knitted his brows for a second before giving a broad smile, exposing the rotting black stumps of his teeth.

'Oh yes, Sergeant, I remember him well. A charming man, and most gallant.'

McGillivray stood to attention and slapped the veteran hard on the face. The veteran's crutches scrabbled for grip on the slippery cobbles as he hopped sideways to maintain his balance.

'Jesus, Sergeant, what was that for? That's no way to treat an old comrade.'

'You are a coward and an impostor, Mr McNeill. You have no title to the uniform which you disgrace.'

Allerdyce wondered whether the sergeant was about to kick the supposed veteran's crutches from under him, but

McGillivray stood stock still as the cripple turned, spat on the cobbles, and swung away on his crutches.

'What was that about, Sergeant?'

'That man is a fraud, sir. He never served with Her Majesty's armed forces.'

'Are you sure?'

'The Ninety-First don't have kilts, sir. And the man had the temerity to claim to know my youngest brother, who served with the Ninety-Third.'

'I'm sorry, Sergeant.'

'I expect he bought old bits of uniform from a rag dealer to pass himself off as an old soldier. We could arrest him, sir, for personation.' The sergeant looked after the impostor, who was swinging his way towards the High Street.

'Sergeant, we have an appointment at the castle to interview Frederick Bothwell-Scott. That duty must take priority.'

'Very well, sir.'

They resumed their progress towards the castle, climbing up the broad slope of the Lawnmarket.

'Did you know anything of Brigadier Bothwell-Scott when you were in the army?' asked Allerdyce.

'I was never favoured with a direct word from him, sir, but I knew him well enough by his actions in the Crimea.'

'Such as?'

'I regret, sir, he was not well regarded by the men. He was briefly in active command of our regiment and led us rather poorly.'

'What happened?'

'A few days after landing in the Crimea, sir, we had to advance across the River Alma. The Russians held the heights above us, and they were firing artillery down into our columns. It was mayhem, sir – heads and limbs being blown into the air by exploding shells – and there was nothing we could do about it until we could storm their cannons. There were French grenadiers advancing beside us, and they were having a hot time too. We couldn't see the Russians, sir, they were hidden by the ridge, all we could see was the ordnance flying above our heads and the shells landing in our midst. At last, as we reached the brow of the hill, we saw a line of Russian soldiers, their rifles ready to fire down on us to finish the job their cannon had started so well. We formed a line under the orders of our junior officers and loaded and aimed our rifles. Just as we were about to fire we heard the order from Colonel Bothwell-Scott to cease fire and lower our guns. He said we were about to fire into a French column which had already captured the heights. Now, sir, I'm not saying that I can tell a Frenchman from a Russian at 300 feet, but the gentlemen on the ridge were most certainly aiming their weapons in an attempt to kill us. Thank God, sir, at that stage Sir Colin Campbell rode up and saw instantly that the colonel had made a fatal mistake. He took command himself and ordered us immediately to fire into the enemy and storm the heights. As we did so, the Russians scattered before us and the day was carried without further unnecessary loss of life.'

'So, at least Sir Frederick's orders were corrected before they could be damaging?'

'I regret very much, sir, that that was the least of the trouble we had from Sir Frederick Bothwell-Scott. Having been removed from active command of soldiers in the field, he was appointed to responsibility for distribution of supplies. Lest he feel humiliated by this, he was promoted by Lord Raglan to the rank of brigadier. It was in that capacity, sir, that he killed more men by neglect of his duty than he could ever have killed in battle.'

As they passed the ragged school they could hear the rhythmic chanting of times tables. McGillivray continued, 'Sir Frederick's entire challenge was organising the forces available to him so that supplies were unloaded from ships, transported to front lines which were no more than five miles distant from the harbour at Balaclava, and distributed according to need. In all this he failed utterly. The story we heard up at the front line was that Sir Frederick had taken his removal from active command very badly and was perpetually drunk. He wouldn't do anything to organise the supplies, and he punished as insubordination any attempt by anyone else to remedy the situation. I can't vouch for the truth of that rumour, sir – all I know is that there were ships full of winter clothes and food lying rotting at anchor in Balaclava harbour with no one stirring a finger to unload them, and that even when anything was finally unloaded it sat decaying in warehouses on the harbourside because no one had sent out the requisition forms which would allow the goods to be released to the army. I'm sorry, sir, if I bear some prejudice against Sir Frederick. It's just that I associate him indelibly with the death of my poor brother.'

'I'm sorry, Sergeant,' said Allerdyce. 'What happened?'

'It may be unfair to blame Sir Frederick directly, sir. Perhaps I might as well blame winter itself for being so harsh in the Crimea. But, when I think of poor Aeneas dying of hypothermia in the sleet while he stood bravely at his post in the trenches in front of Sebastopol, I can't help thinking that a woollen overcoat and a bowl of porridge would have been enough to keep him alive. It's a bitter thought, sir, but it's un-Christian of me to blame any one man.'

The policemen were left waiting in the brigadier's vast office.

The dark wood panelling was interrupted by paintings of old generals in various attitudes of disdain or anger, and lines of red-coated soldiers advancing into different eras of slaughter by sword, musket or artillery. The huge wooden desk supported a sword, laid lengthways on a stand, a decanter of whisky and a glass, and some token papers. Behind the desk was a portrait of the unsmiling, heavily moustached features of Brigadier Sir Frederick Bothwell-Scott, 8th Duke of Dornoch, sitting in full Highland dress as he scowled at the artist, and above that, the glazed eyes of the stuffed-and-mounted head of a ten-pointer stag.

Allerdyce sat drumming his fingers against the desk. He started to whistle gently – a banal little tune from his last visit to the music hall that he couldn't quite get out of his mind.

At last the silence was broken by the muffled flushing of a water closet. A few seconds later a hidden door opened in the panelling, to the right of the brigadier's portrait. The new duke of Dornoch emerged, his red tunic undone, still fastening the fly buttons of his tartan trousers.

'You must be the policemen?'

'Yes, sir.'

'Know who did it yet?'

'No. We'd like to ask you some questions.'

'Well, it bloody well wasn't me so I don't know what I can do for you.'

The brigadier sat down. He was the exact facial image of his portrait, except that the artist had not fully captured the broken veins and the redness of his complexion. He poured himself a whisky and sat back.

'Sir,' asked Allerdyce, 'do you have any idea who might have killed your brother?'

'I'm not a bloody detective, am I? How should I know?'

'Can you think of anyone who might have a particular resentment against him?'

'You don't get to a position of honour in society without people resenting you for it. But no, I can't think of anyone who'd specifically want to murder him.'

Allerdyce took an envelope from the inside pocket of his jacket. He opened it and removed the telegram which had arrived on the afternoon of the late duke's disappearance. He held it out to the brigadier.

'Does this mean anything to you, sir?'

The brigadier took it and, for a couple of seconds, appeared to have difficulty focusing on it before he read it out loud.

'"Mine all mine. Meet at the well at midnight."'

'So? Can you shed any light on the message, sir?'

The brigadier furrowed his brows and squinted again at the telegram. He turned it round, and turned it upside down, as if he could shake some truth out of it. At length he punched the air and seemed, for an instant, to smile.

'I have it gentlemen. It's obvious.'

'Is it, sir?'

'Well, it is to me. I think I should be appointed to the detective force. I clearly have more aptitude for it than you, gentlemen.'

Allerdyce tried not to let his face reflect the insult. The brigadier continued.

'My brother's body was recovered from a mineshaft, wasn't it?'

'We understood it to be a well, sir.'

'You were not fully informed, then. The shaft in which my brother met his end is decorated as an ornamental well, and has water in it, but it was originally a mineshaft. As you know, my family have substantial mining interests on our estates in Linlithgowshire. Most of the reserves are deep below the surface, and have only become accessible in modern times. Some more superficial reserves have, however, been worked for many centuries. The "well" from which William was recovered was a medieval mineshaft – a bottle mine is the correct term I believe. The grounds at Dalcorn are riddled with these shafts, but that's the only one that's been kept open. A sort of memorial.'

'So,' asked Allerdyce, 'how does that lead us to the murderer?'

'Think about mines, gentlemen. Is there anyone connected with the mines who has a resentment against my brother? I can think of one clear person.'

'Who is . . .?'

'James Semple of the Amalgamated Fraternity of Scottish Miners. He's the seditionist who led my brother's miners out on strike when market forces meant he had to cut their wages. He got dismissed for it, of course, along with the other strikers and he and his family were thrown out of the company's cottage. We made sure that every mine-owner and factory-owner in Britain knew not to offer him employment. These were the wise precautions my brother had to take to avoid the spread of industrial sedition. Mutiny is mutiny, whether it's in the army or in the mines. It's only a shame that we can't blow the industrial mutineers from the cannons.'

'So you think Semple would want to kill your brother for revenge?'

'I suppose so.'

'Why do you think he would arrange to meet your brother at midnight, on your brother's estate?'

'I don't know. Presumably you fellows can fill in the details. That's what you do, isn't it?'

'I think we might need some more evidence to be able to charge Mr Semple.'

'Well, thrash it out of him, then. That's what we do in the army. And hang him quick. The worst you'll have done is to rid the world of another verminous socialist. He's got be punished for what he's done.'

Allerdyce shifted in his chair and flicked over another page of his notebook.

'How has your brother's death affected you, sir?'

'What sort of a bloody impertinent question is that?'

'Merely one asked from professional interest, sir.'

'Well, it's a bloody awful thing to happen, isn't it? But you get used to death in this job, and it isn't all bad.'

'Not all bad?'

'I'm sorry for William, of course, but it's been an upturn in my own fortunes. I'm getting a promotion out of this – the army thinks dukes should rank at least as major-generals. And I can't pretend that I don't welcome having the entire revenues of the family's properties.'

'The entire revenues, sir? The late duke made no provision for the duchess in the event of his death?'

'No. Why the hell should he leave anything to that fallow bitch?'

Allerdyce raised his eyebrows.

The brigadier continued, 'My brother managed to avoid marriage for as long as he decently could. He was a wise man – I've managed to avoid marriage entirely and I can't say I feel any the worse for it. But William had the responsibility of perpetuating the family line hanging over him, as our mother reminded him more and more forcibly from year to year. She didn't want the estates passing to a bastard or a stranger. So she ground into him the notion that he had to get married. She also harangued him to recognise the wisdom of marrying his cousin Josephine – she was the sole heir to the fortune which her side of the family had made in

America. It would bring the money home to where it belongs. Well, gentlemen, the whole thing was a bloody disaster from start to finish. Generations of fine breeding had generated a narrow-hipped bitch who couldn't drop a living child. She was nineteen years old when William married her, she's twenty-six now, and she's never sprogged. There isn't going to be any fortune either – it's all gone in the American wars. And she's turned out to be an opinionated shrew. The whole thing was a complete bloody disaster, gentlemen, a daily curse on all our lives. I've a good mind to turn her out of Dalcorn House so that I can enjoy my property in peace.'

Allerdyce grasped at the lead which the brigadier had thrown.

'You mentioned a bastard, sir. Anyone we should be interested in?'

The brigadier knocked back his whisky and poured some more.

'How the hell should I know? William was a man of the world. It was his business what he got up to. I've told you who must have killed William – what else do you need to know?'

'You've suggested James Semple, sir. I just wonder whether there are any other connections with the family we should know about.'

'I've told you everything you need to know. Now, just run along and catch that bloody seditionist if you'd be so kind. I have work to do here.' The brigadier took some papers in his hand, squinted at them, and shuffled them into a different order.

Allerdyce folded away his notebook and stood up to leave. The sergeant followed his lead. The brigadier tottered unsteadily to his feet. He leaned forward over the desk, supporting himself with one hand and holding the glass in the other, and peered at the purple ribbon on McGillivray's chest.

'Victoria Cross?'

'Yes, sir,' answered McGillivray, standing straight.

'Where?'

'Lucknow, sir.'

The brigadier sat back down, heavily, sloshing whisky from the glass on to his tartan trousers.

'Ha, India. Bit different from the Crimea. I didn't get anything from the Crimea except this bloody sword from a Russian officer. Not a single medal for all the work I did to clothe and feed an entire bloody army. And that was a proper bloody war. And then Colin Campbell goes spreading medals around like bloody confetti in India, just for putting down a few darkies. Rather devalues the thing, don't you agree?'

Allerdyce looked towards McGillivray. The sergeant's face had gone quite white, and the colour had drained from his lips. His fists were clenched. Allerdyce worried for a second that the sergeant might actually reach across the desk and strike the brigadier.

McGillivray slowly raised his hand and Allerdyce braced himself to interpose himself between the two soldiers. But the sergeant opened his fist and raised his open hand in a military salute.

The brigadier staggered back up from his chair and, sloppily, returned the salute. McGillivray about-turned and marched out of the office.

The brigadier, leaning forwards on the desk, addressed Allerdyce. 'The lower ranks can be splendid when they're loyal, but once they go bad they need to be exterminated. I trust you know how to deal with Mr Semple.'

Allerdyce looked the brigadier in his rheumy eye but saw no reaction. He turned and followed the sergeant out of the room.

ALLISON DEEDS

'Then we turned the corner,' Mersey said, pausing to take a sip of cold water, 'and the truck came across the yellow lines. Our car was pinned against the mountain.' Shakily, she made her hands into layers. 'Truck, car, mountain. Like a sandwich.'

Mersey had woken early that morning; asking desperately about her friends, surprised to learn it was already Monday. The soft beep of the heart monitor had calmed her and she'd spent the morning staring at the screen, watching her life being measured out in a pale green line. Officer Forest had arrived sometime after eleven. Mersey couldn't bear to look him in the eyes. She had answered his questions and now she wished he would just leave.

'Where exactly did the switch in drivers occur? Do you remember what time of day? Was it before or after you passed Woodburn?' He ran his fingers over his short white moustache, a habit Mersey was quickly growing tired of. His voice was kind, the sort of voice you would expect to come from this older, overweight police officer who looked more like Santa Claus than law enforcement. Mersey sighed, folding her hands in her lap and then unfolding them again, slowly.

'It was after. Definitely after. I remember there was a school bus ahead of us that pulled off towards Woodburn. I'm not sure what time, I wasn't wearing my watch.' Mersey took a deep breath, wanting to close her eyes again. She was going to have to get used to being alone and she wanted to start now.

'Did you notice anyone driving behind you before the scenic pull-off?'

The scratch of pen on paper made Mersey want to cry. She watched the door to the room, hoping a nurse or someone would walk in and interrupt, but no one did.

'I can't do this right now. I'm sorry.'

'That's fine. I understand. I'll come back tomorrow. If you remember anything I've left my number with the nurses. Thanks again for your time.' Mersey turned away and watched his reflection in the dark window, watched him shut the door quietly behind him, and then closed her eyes.

It was a vacation they had planned for months. Over the last year they had drifted apart, something they all wanted to remedy, and Sketch's twenty-fourth birthday was the perfect excuse. A chance to get closer, a chance to get back to the kids they once were together. They planned to spend the weekend up at Treasure and Nick's cabin. They left early on Friday afternoon, hoping to get to the cabin before dark, which came much earlier in the mountains.

They packed Treasure's light blue Honda full of their favourite old movies and junk food, as well as bags of clothes for the weekend. Nick teased Treasure about the amount of clothing she insisted on taking, and only got her to agree on one suitcase by reminding her that she had clothes at the cabin already. The drive to the cabin would only be three hours long, and mostly through the scenic mountains. It was late spring and a wonderful, sunny day.

Treasure had just taken the wheel, with Sketch sitting in the passenger seat because it was his birthday. Mersey sat, at first, in the middle seat in the back, but had now moved to the far left, behind Treasure, trailing her fingers out the window and smiling. Dylan sat close to her, and Nick next to him. They listened to David Bowie and started listing their favourite movies alphabetically. When they came to M, Sketch added *The Matrix*, as everyone knew he would.

They turned a corner, facing a large uphill stretch of road. A semi-truck with a lime-green cab was coming down the hill in the other lane. Treasure reached her hand out the window to wave hello, and just then, as 'Space Oddity' came to a close and there was a pause before the next song, just then when Nick threw a cheese curl at the back of Sketch's head, laughing, and Dylan took the nearly empty soda bottle from Mersey's hand and lifted it to drink the last—

Just then the truck turned sharply and Treasure slammed on the brakes. The truck hit their car on the front-left corner and slammed them through the guardrail, crushing them against the grey rock of the mountain.

Treasure and Nick, together for nearly all of their twenty-five years, became one person in their deaths. Parts of Sketch were ground into the rock of the mountain. The driver of the truck survived and, after lifting an unconscious Mersey from the wreckage and using his cellphone to call the police, he sat down on the side of the road and smoked the last of his pack of Lucky Strikes. Then, taking his ivory-handled straight razor which he always carried for self-defence, he cut his neck nearly all the way through.

'I don't think I can do this . . .' Mersey's voice came out as a scratchy whisper; she was shaking her head and trembling. Sandy squatted down beside her, trying to break the grip Mersey had on the armrest of the wheelchair. Sketch's parents, Sandy and John, had come to get her early that morning. They had heard Officer Forest was coming back and wanted to get her away from his questions. They were going to take her to their house for the night, or a few nights if she would stay. Sandy hated the idea of Mersey sitting alone in the apartment with her memories.

The car was waiting by the kerb. John was sitting behind the wheel, too obviously not watching as the nurses and Sandy tried to convince Mersey to get into the car. Sandy's hands were gentle, the nurses' hands weren't.

'Mersey, we have to get you home and home is quite a ways from here. It's only an hour and we'll be right there with you. Come on, Mersey, you can do this . . .' Mersey just kept shaking her head, crying. She couldn't get into the car. She couldn't do it. Not now, not ever. She tried wheeling herself backwards, away from the car, back up to the hospital room where there was a comfortable bed and enough misery to keep her from really facing the truth. The nurses stood behind her, feet braced against the wheels, refusing to let her retreat. Why didn't they understand that she just couldn't do this? She tried to scream, but her voice had left her.

·She kept her eyes closed, moving her feet along the ground, trying to back up, trying to rewind her life, back to the hospital room and further, back to Friday afternoon so she could stop this from happening. She should have told them she was too sick to go. She should have told them that a weekend at the local hotel would be the same. She should have stopped them, somehow. She should have been driving the car; maybe she would have been able to stop the accident. She should have changed something.

'*Les Miserables* doesn't *technically* count as a movie, Treasure. I mean, it was a musical first and foremost. The movie is only a recorded version of the musical . . .' Sketch was arguing, a big smile on his face. Mersey watched the fingers of his left hand trace patterns ceaselessly on his knee, his black jeans failing to register the imprint left there by his fingers. She took a big sip of the soda, passing the bottle to Dylan and taking his hand into hers. Next to him, Nick crunched his cheese curls and tried to wipe the orange grime from his fingers, shaking his head.

David Bowie's voice floated out the open windows. They turned the corner and began a long stretch of steep road. Treasure reached her hand out of the car window, waving happily at an oncoming truck with a lime-green cab.

'How about *The Lion King*, then? That's definitely a movie. Also a musical, but still a movie . . .'

'Fine, *The Lion King*. What about M?' Treasure smiled at Mersey in the rear-view mirror as Sketch leapt out of his seat with excitement and Dylan mouthed Sketch's answer along with him.

'*The Matrix!*'

Dylan tilted his head back as he tried to get the last drops of Mersey's soda from the bottom of the bottle. Mersey smiled, David Bowie's 'Space Oddity' was just finishing on the tape, and Nick threw a half-eaten cheese curl at the back of Sketch's head, laughing.

Treasure began to scream as she slammed on the brakes.

Mersey must have passed out. When she opened her eyes she was sitting in the back seat of the car with her seatbelt on, Sandy holding her hand and patting her hair down, making a shushing sound like a mother trying to soothe a frightened child.

She didn't look out the window. She was sitting where Nick had been. The passenger seat ahead of her was empty. Sketch would have been sitting there with his legs folded beneath him, tracing patterns into his black jeans.

John was talking, his voice too calm. There was no music playing. Mersey tried to listen. She reached up to the manual door lock and slipped it into place. She tightened her seat belt. John was still talking. Mersey reached up to make sure the door was locked; it was. She felt for the seat-belt catch, tugged on it to make sure it was fastened and then pulled the strap tighter. She tried to listen to what John was saying. Was the door locked? Mersey pressed down on the lock, hard, and then dropped her hands down to see if her seat belt was fastened properly. She moved her hand quickly to the door lock, just to make sure. Sandy took Mersey's hands in hers, folded them in Mersey's lap and kept shushing. John was talking.

'I remember what it was like for Sam when we first moved here. He never had many friends in Chicago, but when we moved here it just got worse. They all made fun of him for being too skinny, too pale. For spending too much time in the art studio and not enough on the football field . . .' He paused. Mersey knew John only referred to Sketch by his given name when he was angry with him, and maybe just now he was. Mersey wanted to make it stop. She wanted to go away where it was quiet. She didn't want to hear John's words, didn't want to see Sandy's tears. She didn't want any of this. She wanted everything to be the way it had been.

'I don't know if any of us ever really thanked you for being so nice to him. We did appreciate it, though, and so did he. I remember the way he talked about you when he met you . . . Mersey this and Mersey that. Her hair, her friends, her everything. Sandy and I always thought that you had been well named. Mercy . . .'

They were both crying now, the silent, awkward tears of parents.

The trees were just beginning to bud. They had loaded Treasure's Honda with chips and chocolate and Oreo cookies. Sketch usually had to sit in the back seat because he was always the fifth in this group of five. Since it was his birthday, though, they made an exception and let him sit in the passenger seat. Mersey thought it was funny that he could get so excited about something so small, but Sketch had always been like that.

Treasure put the David Bowie tape on as soon as they got back on the road after switching drivers. His voice blended well with the open road and the cool spring day. They started listing their favourite movies in alphabetical order. A game they used to play on paper when bored during study halls or, more recently, in long chains of emails during the work day. When they got to M, Sketch said *The Matrix*, as they all knew he would. David Bowie was gliding through the last few chords of 'Space Oddity'. Treasure reached out of her window to wave hello to a truck with a lime-green cab. The tape switched to silence before the next song. Nick threw a small cheese curl at the back of Sketch's head. Dylan took the bottle of soda from Mersey's hand and tilted his head back to drink the last few drops.

Then everything went green. Mersey was screaming. She could see Dylan's head tilted back in the warm spring sunlight and then everything went green.

Mersey pulled the sesame seeds off a tiny sandwich containing what was probably chicken salad. She sighed; tired after a fitful night spent dreaming in the colour green. She hadn't wanted to be at the funeral service. She wished she were anywhere else in the world. Everyone was wearing too much perfume, trying to mask their fear. The chemical smells began to give her a headache. Dylan's parents, Cindy and Frank, stood quite close to Mersey, eyeing her uncomfortably and talking in low whispers.

'Most of the mourners have been seated. It's just the families left now, so if you could line up like we discussed we'll lead you into the church.' The minister gave a sad smile and left the room. Mersey looked across at Nick's older brother, Jamie. He had asked to escort her down the aisle, but had been vetoed. Apparently there was a certain way these things were done, and the minister had stated that Mersey would walk by herself.

The caskets were set at the front of the church, closed. There were so many flowers. Flowery wreaths with names on them perched near the caskets on small steps, looking final. Mersey sat in the first pew next to the aisle. Best seat in the house.

The minister stood and gave his 'they are back in the hands of the Lord' speech and led them all in a song of sadness. Mersey watched and listened; she stood when everyone stood and sat back down when she was the only one left standing. She couldn't take her eyes off the flowery wreaths. Dylan, Samuel, Treasure, Nicholas. Heart-shaped wreaths of white roses. Apart from Treasure: she had four yellow roses among the white. Dylan wouldn't have wanted white flowers. He never liked the colour white; he said it was too boring. Sketch hated white. His parents knew that. Black flowers would have been more appropriate – or deep red. Nick wouldn't care what colour his flowers were, but he would have known that yellow was Treasure's favourite colour when she was eight, but not now. Treasure's favourite colour was peach now, because you could never tell if it was red or orange or yellow. They should have asked Mersey. She would have set them straight.

A lot of their old teachers were there, townspeople stopped by to give their condolences and Mersey felt like she had become a sideshow. The mayor of their city was even there. It all felt a little surreal. They all wanted to tell her how tragic it was, how those kids were *really* special. Mersey couldn't help herself getting angry at them. Did they think she didn't know? Dylan had all but failed English in high school and here was their English teacher trying to tell Mersey what a great guy he'd been, and how he'd had such potential. Such a tragedy, they all said. Such a tragedy . . . they were all so young. Such a tragedy.

Dylan's boss made a speech and Mersey noticed he had the rest of their names written down on a note card. Dylan and Nick's old baseball coach said something about how they all needed to keep a hold of hope for the future even in the midst of this tragedy. Mersey wondered at the falsity of it. The wrong flowers and people who hadn't known them, giving speeches. They were getting it all wrong.

Treasure's parents stood, heads held high, and said something about how beautiful Treasure had been, how much like an angel. Mersey thought they should have said something about how they thought they were better than her and smarter than her and how they didn't think her chosen career in music was good enough. How they had spent countless hours arguing at her about Nick and how she should marry someone whose family was more like theirs, meaning rich.

Dylan's mother trembled while she spoke of the hopes they'd had for their son. They included Mersey in their hopes, gazing down at her from a few rows away. Mersey looked away, down at her feet, and tried to tune them out. She remembered hearing Dylan's side of countless conversations with his parents, refusing to apologise for his actions and trying to defend his decision to marry her. Mersey tried not to feel angry with them, not to shout out that she was the only one who had really loved him for who he was.

Nick's brother Jamie stood, tears in his eyes, and talked about how strong his brother had been, how happy. How he was so wilful and so dedicated. He had wanted certain things in life and he hadn't let anything stand in his way . . . Mersey could feel his sadness. He sat back down halfway through a word, sobbing.

Sandy shook as she talked about Sketch, her two daughters holding her hands, holding her up. She spoke only of Sketch's incredible talent, of how he had such vision and such poise. How there would be an empty space in everyone's life now he had gone.

Mersey couldn't bring herself to talk. She couldn't stand the staring. No one would have listened, anyway. The only ones who had ever listened to her were lying in closed caskets behind the wrong-coloured roses.

LICHEN
(extract from a novel in progress)

ANN BURNETT

'I'm just going out for a drink with Beth and Marion, remember? I told you, Mother, I'll only be an hour or so. Just for a quick drink.'

'But, Janis, you don't go to pubs,' she's saying. 'You haven't been in a pub for years. Not since you left Michael.'

God, don't I know it. But this is the new me, breaking out a bit. It's taken me all my courage to agree to this and I'm trembling so much I can scarcely get my lipstick on my lips. But I want to do this. I have to do this. And now Mother is making it even more difficult. I take several deep breaths and tell myself over and over again that I will enjoy it. It is beginning to sound like a command – YOU WILL ENJOY IT OR ELSE – but I'm fighting back those wee voices that tell me I can't do it, that I'll never be normal, whatever that is, that I'm doomed to be imprisoned with Mother for all eternity.

'What if I take ill when you're out? You know the doctor said I was to watch my heart.'

She's at it again. Blackmail. Make me feel guilty so I won't go. I could do without this, it's hard enough. It would be so easy to phone Marion and tell her I can't because Mother's taken poorly.

'The doctor said to watch what you eat to protect your heart,' I shout. Her selective deafness has taken hold and she's desperately trying not to hear that I'm leaving. 'You've to stop eating so many sugary things. There's nothing wrong with your heart at the moment.'

Her hand goes to her cheek and I see the liver spots and the raised blue veins like tributaries heading for the river. Her nails are too long and I make a mental note to cut them for her tomorrow. She lowers her head and stares at the carpet.

'You'll be fine!' I bellow. 'I'll be back before you know it. Anyway, you can watch your programmes in peace and I'll put the phone beside you, just in case.'

'I'll just have to not go to the toilet till you come back.' Her voice has a quaver in it.

'You've just been. You won't need. You never go until bedtime.'

'But what if I'm caught short? That fish pie you made isn't agreeing with me. I've got a bit of a pain. I didn't like to say before in case you were offended, but it was too rich for me.'

'Look what you ate that weekend we were away with Ninian.'

'Yes, and look at the pain I had then. Terrible it was, and me not able to say anything to him and having to cover it up from him.'

'Rubbish, Mother. It was only during the night you had the pain. You were fine when you got rid of the wind.' My stomach gives a sympathetic churn as if it's in league with Mother's. It's also trying to tell me to stay in and forget such nonsense as going out for a drink.

I plonk the phone down beside her chair and walk out of the room. In my bedroom, as I reach in for my jacket, a wave of panic roars through me and I clutch the wardrobe door. I try to breathe calmly, try to wait it out. I close my eyes and my head swirls. I stagger over to the bed and flop down on it, groaning. My brain continues its mad whirling, like a dervish. My stomach heaves and I have to rush to the bathroom and empty it of the fish pie. Maybe Mother is right, maybe it was too rich, full of salmonella, tainted, poisonous. Maybe I will phone and call it off. Maybe I won't go.

I brush my teeth, sort my hair, throw on my jacket and head for the door.

'That's me away,' I shout, not waiting for a reply. I can't get the key in the lock of the car door, my hands are shaking so much. But I do, I get in, start it up, and drive off without letting myself think of the enormity of what I am doing.

The pub is noisy and not all that well lit and, at first, I can't see Marion and Beth. Panic tries to get hold of me again, but then I see them waving at me like trees in a gale. I weave my way towards them, trying to put a smile on and look as if this is just something I do every week instead of once in – how long has it been? – ten years. The pub caters for a slightly older clientele than the teenage and early-twenties market, or so I judge by the age of the customers I pass. A lot of them are groups of women in their late twenties and thirties and for a moment I feel that I'm too old for this lark and that a night in with Mother would suit me better. But I shake it off and remember Ninian's warm hand taking mine as we met that first time and I tell myself that if I want a life then this is the start of it all.

Marion and Beth are squashed in at a tiny table with bright pink and blue drinks in front of them. They've kept a seat for me, a small velvet-covered stool, on which I tentatively perch. They're both heavily made-up and wearing glittery tops with black trousers and gold in their ears. Marion is exposing a great deal of shoulder while Beth's midriff is hanging over the waistband of her trousers, though waistband is perhaps not the right term, it being situated somewhat south of her waist. I feel frumpish: I've put on black trousers, but I'm wearing a white blouse with a broderie anglaise trim at the collar. So neat, so prim, so old-fashioned. I can see I've got a lot of catching up to do in the fashion stakes. I smile, though, and slip off my jacket.

Marion looks at Beth and they grin at each other.

'Makeover alert! Makeover alert!' says Marion.

'Where's Trinny and Susannah?' chimes Beth.

'Yes, I know,' I say. 'But at least I'm here.'

'You're turning into your mother,' says Beth.

'I hope not,' I reply. 'She had an illegitimate son fifty years ago who's just turned up on our doorstep.'

I get the reaction. I didn't mean to tell them like that but I certainly get the reaction I'd wished for. For the first time in years, I've said something that has grabbed their attention.

'Hold on,' says Marion. 'Stop right there. This requires another round.'

She gets up and squeezes her way through the crush to the bar. Beth stares at me. At that moment, a microphone whines into life and a man's voice says something unintelligible which is followed by a ripple of applause. A band starts up at about ninety decibels. The beat of the bass throbs through the carpet under my feet. Conversation has to stop. I smile at Beth as we wait for Marion to return from the bar. Beth nods her head in time to the music and I see her lips move as she sings along. She turns to me and says something which I can't hear.

'Pardon?' I shout back.

She mouths, 'Fantastic!' and snaps her fingers and shakes her head so that her hair swings perilously close to her bright blue drink. I watch, mesmerised, as each flick of her head brings her hair closer to the liquid. Suddenly, she grabs her drink and swallows it in one. Marion appears, holding a tray above her head with three glasses sliding back and forth. Somehow they all successfully arrive on the table and a lurid red one is placed in front of me.

Marion mimes 'drink up' to me and I raise the glass to my lips and take a sip. Whatever happened to vodka and Coke? The liquid is sweet, like a soft drink, but not fizzy and I take another sip. It goes over pleasantly and I think I might enjoy it, whatever it is. I make a mental note to find out the name of it. It seems pretty innocuous. The live music spews out of hidden speakers with only occasional interruptions for scattered applause as one song finishes and another begins. They all sound the same to me but I tap my feet in what I hope is time and fix my smile like a painted doll's. It's impossible to talk and anyway, this is obviously what Marion and Beth enjoy. They are both jigging about in their seats, eyes half closed, mouths slightly open. They look faintly ridiculous. Other groups of women seem to be managing to carry on a conversation. They all smoke heavily and drink a lot. Empty glasses collect on the tables and fresh ones are added. Nobody seems to collect the empties and none of the customers take them back to the bar when they order rounds. I feel like an anthropologist in the middle of some strange and exotic tribe.

I find, to my surprise, that I've finished my drink. I wonder if I should offer to buy the next round and if so, what should I order, when Beth jumps to her feet and heads to the bar. This time my drink is muddy brown with a straw. I smile my thanks to her and sip. Coffee-flavoured with a minty undertone. Liquid After Eight. I want to sit back and enjoy it but I'm sitting on that silly stool. I lean back anyway and feel support behind me. I'm just letting my weight be taken by it when it moves and I have to apologise to a plump girl whose back it is. She looks at me a bit oddly but I just grin at her and take another sip. I can feel myself relaxing now and I'm almost enjoying myself. The music seems better too, and I move on the stool along with it. Armchair dancing, I think and giggle. Stool dancing doesn't sound nearly as nice: rude, almost.

The music stops after endless indistinguishable numbers followed by another burst of applause, an unintelligible announcement which rises to a crescendo and then more applause. Marion whistles loudly, her fingers in her mouth. Beth stands up and shouts, 'Yeah, man!' at the departing band. Suddenly, it's quiet again.

'Fab-u-lous!' says Marion. 'They are the greatest, aren't they?' She turns to me and I nod my head as I sip my drink.

'Really good,' I murmur.

'Now,' says Beth, leaning across the table at me, 'what were you telling us about your mother?'

I surprise myself with a giggle. 'Ninian,' I say. 'He's turned up. At long last. The long-lost son nobody knew anything about, not even my father.'

I tell the story, interspersed with gasps and oohs from the two of them.

'What's he like?' asks Beth.

'He's very kind and thoughtful and—'

'No,' says Marion. 'Not that stuff. What's he look like, how old is he and is he loaded?' They both laugh loudly.

A wave of jealousy sweeps over me. He's mine, I want to say. He's my half-brother. He's not available. But he is, I realise. He is available and not to me. He is available to women like Beth and Marion and any number, probably, of the women around us in the pub. But for me, he's out of bounds. He is my blood relation after all. I will have to sit back and watch as sundry women flaunt their charms in front of him and lure him away from us. I will have to watch as he falls in love with someone whom I shall hate on sight and for ever. Just as he has arrived in our lives, he will be enticed away again.

'He's not your type,' I say. 'He's . . . well, over fifty for a start . . .'

'Doesn't bother us. Plenty of cash and a dicky ticker is all we need, isn't it?' Beth and Marion lean in to each other and cackle.

'I don't think he's well off,' I continue. 'He's divorced and he just has a flat in Edinburgh.'

'What kind of flat? Some of those Edinburgh flats are as big as houses,' says Marion.

'Even small flats can be worth half a million,' says Beth.

'It's . . . it's actually outside Edinburgh,' I say, though I really have no idea where his flat is. 'He's not one for material possessions, he's into . . . giving to the poor, serving others . . .'

'*Saint* Ninian, is he?' says Beth and we all laugh, me with relief.

'He loves opera' – I have remembered that it's one of Marion's pet hates – 'and . . . gardening.' I'm pretty sure Beth has never so much as lifted a weed. 'So he won't do for either of you. Sorry, girls.'

'Well, we *are* getting desperate,' says Marion. 'So I think we'll call and look him over anyway.'

I'm tempted to claim he's homosexual or training for the priesthood but I don't. Not yet anyway. Marion drains her glass.

'Drink up, Janis. We've time for another before you have to get back to Mummy.'

'I'll get it,' I say. 'What are you drinking?' I hope they don't say same again as I have no idea what the drinks are. I move the empty glasses towards the middle of the table and stand up.

Beth names some drink I don't quite catch as I'm too busy trying to make my legs straighten. They want to bend and leave me sinking into the floor. Somehow I start out towards the bar, but halfway there I change direction as I see the sign for the ladies. Fortunately, there's a cubicle free and I fall in and collapse in front of the toilet bowl. My head feels heavy and I can only take in small parts of what I'm looking at. And I'm looking at a none-too-clean bowl with splashes of urine on the black seat and a smear of blood down the inside of the pan. But I don't care. I rest my head on the cistern and a tsunami of dizziness crashes over me. I swim against it hopelessly and helplessly until I have to raise my head and vomit my drinks into the bowl. I retch and retch until my guts feel as if they have been punched and bruised.

'You should have eaten something before you came out,' says a voice. It's Marion. I don't have the energy or the ability to tell her about the fish pie.

'Let's get you out of here.' Beth grabs my arms and she and Marion lift me up and help me stand. I actually feel better and the room is standing still and I can focus on their faces.

'Sorry about that,' I mumble. 'It must have been something I ate.'

'No it wasn't,' says Marion. 'You didn't bring up any food. Just the drinks. Fucking expensive they were too, and wasted on you.'

'Sorry,' I say again.

'And *you've* never heaved-ho in a pan before?' says Beth to Marion. 'What about that party at Robert's? When you never even made the toilet and it went all over his feet.'

They laugh and slap each other's arms. We make our way out of the pub, Beth nipping back to our table to collect the bags and jackets. Before I know it, I'm being pushed into a taxi and waved off by them. I wave back as we drive past my parked car. I gaze at it, then let the taxi driver take me home.

THE LEXICON OF LOVE
(extract from a novel in progress)

LES WOOD

*[Campbell and John are identical twins, operating a
Glasgow tattoo parlour but also part of a team of crooks
working for a notorious gangster and drug-dealer, Boddice.
For reasons explained in previous chapters, John has
started an affair with Boddice's wife and, for even more
complex reasons, Campbell has to try to pass himself off
as John when he is next summoned by Boddice's wife for
an illicit liaison. Campbell has arrived at Boddice's house.]*

Campbell swallowed hard and rang the doorbell.

He waited.

There was no sound from inside the house, no movement
that he could see through the frosted glass panels to the side
of the door. He stepped back from the porch and scanned the
building: no signs of life at the upstairs windows. A crust of
snow clung to the roof tiles in patches, looking like a map
of some newly discovered planet. Only the cloud of conden-
sation billowing from the boiler vent at the far corner of the
house gave any indication the place was occupied.

He waited a few minutes. Still nothing. Campbell breathed
a sigh of relief; there was no one home. He turned and started
to head down the driveway, was about to start whistling, pick

up a jaunty wee tune to lighten his step, when he heard the door opening.

'Sorry to keep you waiting.'

He spun round. The woman standing in the doorway was about fifty, maybe older, hair dyed jet black and pulled back into a long ponytail. She was dressed to the nines in a classy cream suit and lots of jewellery, but the fake tan and heavy make-up gave her a severe, brittle edge.

'I could see you on the intercom,' she said, nodding towards the camera lens mounted above the door. 'But the bloody thing's broken; I couldn't activate the buzzer to let you in.'

'That's OK,' Campbell said, a strange fluttering catch in his voice.

'And I was on the phone to Norman, so I couldn't come down right away. He'd forgotten his shaver, was driving back to get it.'

Campbell frowned. Norman? Who was Norman? Was he the . . .? Oh, my God. Dear Jesus in heaven! Norman. She was talking about Boddice.

'Mr Boddice!' he yelped. 'Is he . . .'

'Don't worry,' she said. 'I persuaded him just to buy another one when he got there. He can just throw the old one away.' She laughed. 'He's not coming back. My, the look on your face!' She took him by the hand, led him into the house.

'Ah'm sorry,' he said. 'It's jist that . . .'

'Don't apologise,' she said softly. 'I'm just glad you decided to come back.' She slid her hand behind his neck, drew him towards her. She kissed him. Her tongue, slipping between his teeth, had the dry, metallic taste of cigarettes and coffee.

She pulled back. 'Why don't you go on upstairs? I'll join you in a minute. I just have a couple of things to attend to and then we can have a right good session.'

Campbell hesitated. 'Eh, whit room is it again? Ah wisnae paying too much attention the last time.'

'The last time?' she said. 'What are you talking about? Last time was in the living room. On the sofa. How could you forget?'

Bastard. Campbell was going to throttle John when he got a hold of him. 'Oh aye, Ah know *that*, it's jist that Ah thought, ye know . . .'

'Look, settle down,' she said. 'I appreciate you're a bit nervous.' She smiled. 'Relax. Norman won't be back until tomorrow. We'll be just fine.' She took him by the shoulders, steered him towards the stairs. 'We'll use one of the spare bedrooms this time. I've got it all sorted out. Up to the top landing, second door on the left. I'll not be long.' She sent him on his way with a squeeze of his buttocks.

Campbell climbed the stairs to the upper floor. He had never been in Boddice's house before. Christ, he had never even passed the front gate. This was strictly out-of-bounds territory. Not for the likes of him. Or his daft brother. Or any of them, for that matter. As far as he knew, none of the team had more than the vaguest notion of where Boddice actually lived. What the fuck was John thinking? Not only had he come into Boddice's house, his inner sanctum – that was bad enough – but he was shagging his wife. His bloody wife! This was just about the riskiest thing imaginable. And the stupid bastard had now involved Campbell as well. If Boddice ever found out, they would both be dead men. And not just dead, but tortured, beaten, hot boiled eggs shoved up their arseholes, dipped in baths of acid and made to beg for sweet mercy beforehand. Campbell had a brief vision of Prentice and Kyle showing up at his door in the wee small hours one night, baseball bats in hand. Death would be the least of his worries.

He arrived at the top landing, took his bearings. Fuck, but this house was big. The hallway stretched into the distance, all polished floorboards, expensive rugs and fancy wall hangings. Tasteful stuff. Campbell thought he recognised a Vettriano hanging on one of the walls – the real deal, not a print – just a wee one, but it must have cost a fair whack. He found the bedroom and went in, the door closing behind him with a tiny snick, like someone tutting. The curtains were drawn, shutting out the daylight, and tealight candles burned in coloured glass holders on the bedside cabinets. An incense burner sent little coils of patchouli-scented smoke towards the ceiling. The bed was massive – Campbell thought you could probably get a decent five-a-side game on there. Red and black pillows were scattered against the wrought-iron bedstead and the black silk sheets were turned down. A regular boudoir, Campbell thought. Man, if this was one of the spare bedrooms, what must the master bedroom be like?

He sat on the bed and rubbed his palms on his trousers. There was still time to do a runner. Wherever Boddice's wife had gone, he could just bolt down the stairs, out the door and down the driveway with the fancy wee lights in the grass borders. Let John deal with the fallout. But if he did that, the whole set-up with himself and John would be exposed. Boddice would find out.

He had no option but to go through with it.

Campbell kicked off his shoes and peeled off his socks, cursing John under his breath. What a fucking mess. He stood and stripped down to his underwear, placing his clothes on a wicker chair in the corner. He settled on the edge of the bed, drumming his fingers on his knee. There was something else worrying him. Boddice's wife was not exactly his type. She was a bit beyond his normal age range and, if he was being honest, she looked as if she'd seen better days. Was John really that desperate? Then again, John had always been an opportunist – given the chance he would shag the buttonhole in a fur coat. Campbell considered himself to be a bit more discerning. And that was the problem. He was afraid he wouldn't be able to perform, wouldn't get it up.

He went through to the en suite and ran the cold tap. He splashed some water on his face, inspected his pasty reflection in the mirror. His pupils were dilated, less to do with the gloom of the bedroom than the fear of standing in nothing more than his scraggy grey boxers in Boddice's spare bedroom, waiting for the man's wife (*his wife!*) to show up. Christ, what if Boddice had forgotten more than his shaver? What if he'd decided to cancel the whole fucking trip, come home, spend a nice relaxing weekend with the missus in front of the plasma screen, a few glasses of wine and an early night, a wee bit of reading before nodding off? What if he was pulling into the driveway right now? Climbing the stairs, wondering what *was* that smell of hippy-shit perfume coming from the spare bedroom? Has someone been sleeping in *my* bed?

Campbell heard the bedroom door open and close. His heart leapt in his chest. Jesus, Mary and Joseph and all the saints with their shiny fucking halos, this was it. He was a dead man.

Campbell peered out from the en suite. Boddice's wife leaned against the bedroom door – she had changed out of her suit, slipped into something more comfortable as it were. She let her white satin dressing gown slide to the floor as she locked the door behind her.

'Like what you see?' she asked.

Campbell stared. Her hair was let down from its ponytail and she was wearing what appeared to be the contents of page one of the Ann Summers lingerie catalogue – black stockings and suspenders, black push-up bra and crotchless panties. The low-level lighting helped, of course, but Campbell had to concede she looked sexy. She stood with her hands on her hips. 'Well?' she said. 'Does this turn you on, lover?'

Campbell cleared his throat. 'Yes,' he replied. 'It does.' He felt himself begin to harden, pushing and throbbing against his boxers.

She sashayed over to him, dragged her fingernails across his chest and looked down between his legs. 'So . . .' She smiled, licked her lips. 'Are we going to set him free then? He seems to be knocking at the door down there.' She reached towards him and tugged his boxers down. His cock sprang free. She gasped and jumped back. 'Oh my God!'

'What?' he asked. He'd never had *that* reaction before. 'What is it?'

'You're . . . you're . . .'

'What?!'

'You're . . . hairy!'

'Hairy? What are you talking about?'

'Last week,' she said. 'Last week, you were bald, shaved down there. You said it was a porno trick, made your cock look bigger.'

Campbell put his hand to his head. John – the bastard – he was setting him up! He must have believed the yarn that guy had told them at the tattoo shop, shaved his pubes, the idiot. But he conveniently neglected to let Campbell know that little secret before he sent him off to shag the boss's wife. The arsehole! It was deliberate. Campbell would cut off more than John's pubes the next time he saw him. He had to think fast.

'Oh aye, that!' he said. 'Ah wunnered whit ye were talkin aboot.' He shrugged and gave a short laugh. 'It's nae big deal. We're aw hairy guys in oor faimily, huv tae shave two, some-times three times a day. Jist grows back like wildfire, cannae contain it.' He pointed to his groin. 'Same doon there, wan day, oot wi the shavin foam an a plastic Bic, coupla days later – whoosh! It's back!' She was frowning. Campbell could see the doubt on her face. He tried a different tack. 'It's a virility thing. Aw that testosterone.'

She raised an eyebrow. 'Really?'

'Maist definitely. Full tae the brim wi it.'

She placed her hand on his cock, sliding it down the shaft, and flashed her eyes at him. 'Why don't we put that to the test then?' She took his hand and led him to the bed. She pulled back the sheets and clambered on. 'Let's try it this way this time.' She knelt on the bed, tucking pillows under her chest and settling herself on to them. 'OK,' she said. 'I'm ready for you, lover. Roger me rigid.'

Campbell shook his head. This was it – the point of no return. He knelt behind her, looked down. He saw the tattoo John had done for her – a red devil on her left buttock, complete with evil grin and a wee trident. Not bad, but Campbell knew he would have done it better, made the grin a bit more wicked, put a little twinkle in the devil's eyes. Maybe used a deeper shade of red.

'What are you waiting for?' she asked. 'C'mon, baby, do me.'

'Sorry,' he muttered. He took a deep breath and guided himself into her. His cock slipped in easily and she wriggled slightly, making herself more comfortable.

'Ooh, that's nice,' she said.

He began to move steadily, setting up a rhythm that would keep him going for a while without losing it too soon.

He was about to reach round, find her clit, when she lifted her head from the pillows. 'Make the noises again. They really turned me on the last time.'

'Noises?' said Campbell. What the fuck was she talking about?

'Yes,' she said. 'Like you did before. C'mon, lover, pump me hard and do the noises.'

Campbell began to falter, lose his rhythm. What noises? He could feel himself becoming soft.

She pushed back on to him, moving her hips against him. His cock perked up again.

Noises? Noises? What the fuck had John been doing?

'Come on, babes,' she said. 'The noises.'

He made a stab at it. 'Eeeee, eeeee . . .'

She turned her head, looked at him over her shoulder. 'What the hell are you doing?' she asked.

'Making noises?' he suggested.

'That's not the ones you did the last time, the ones that got my juices going.' She began thrusting, increasing her speed, making him follow suit. He'd need to be careful – if it got too fast too soon, he'd end up shooting early. She gripped the spars of the bedstead, throwing her head back and sending her hair falling along her shoulders. 'The noises – c'mon, sweetcheeks, same as before. Do it!'

He was at a total loss. He never even knew John made *any* sounds when he was shagging, let alone what the fuck they might actually be. Maybe he should just own up, tell her the truth, take the consequences. After all, she couldn't very well complain to Boddice, could she? *Could she?* That might be the best solution. He would . . . he would . . .

He had a brainwave.

'You first,' he said.

'What?' She buried her head in the pillow.

'You make them first this time,' he said. 'And I'll join in.'

She laughed. 'You dirty bastard,' she said. 'You really do know how to make me hot!' She slowed down, stretched luxuriously. 'All right, you're on.' She slipped off his cock, turned round and pushed Campbell on to his back. 'But if I'm gonna do it, I want *you* underneath *me!*'

She pinned him on the bed and straddled him, guiding him back inside. She stretched behind her, undoing her bra. Her breasts fell out, massive and pendulous. She ran her hands through her hair, rocking back and forth, sliding along his shaft. Moving slowly at first, with each stroke out she moaned 'hoo!' and 'haa!' with each stroke back. 'Hoo-haa! Hoo-haa!'

Hoo-haa? In the name of the wee man − what had John been thinking? *Hoo-haa?* Did he do that every single time? What a prat. Campbell fought back the urge to laugh.

She settled down on top of him, letting her tits brush against his chest. 'Hoo-haa, hoo-haa, c'mon, baby, join in. Hoo-haa!' She was increasing the pace, pushing him deeper inside her.

'Hoo-haa . . .' he said weakly.

'No, lover, same as you did before. I want you to shout it! HOOOO-HAAAA!' she screamed.

Christ Almighty, this was fucking ridiculous. Was she serious? 'Hooo-haaa!' he yelled.

'That's it! God, I love this so much − do me, baby, do me hard! Hoo-haa, hoo-haa!' She was moving faster still. Campbell could almost imagine a guy at the foot of the bed beating a big kettledrum, oil glistening on his bare chest. Hoooo − left hand, haaaa − right hand. Hooo! Haaa! Ramming speed!

He could feel himself getting close; it wouldn't be long now. He decided to join in, full gusto. They rocked together, thrusting faster and faster, Campbell pumping his hips up into her. 'Hoo-haa, hoo-haa!' they shouted in unison. 'Hoo-haa, hoo-haa!' faster and faster. 'Hoohaahoohaahoohaahoohaa hoohaahoohaa . . .' Campbell was beginning to hyperventilate – he thought he might faint. He felt himself on the edge, tried to hold back for a few more seconds. He gave a final thrust – 'Hoooooo-HAAAAAAA!' He exploded and arched his back, held her above him, his cock twitching and pulsing inside her.

He collapsed, exhausted, on to the bed. She was laughing. 'That was even better than last time,' she said. Campbell suppressed a smirk – that was one he could store up for a bit of ammunition later. *Better than last time, eh, John? What do you think of that?* 'Only one thing . . .' she went on.

'Oh, what's that then?' he asked.

'Well, last time I got myself off too, you know? My little cherry bomb. And it was just delicious for me, remember?'

'Eh . . . aye . . .' Campbell said.

She rolled off him on to her back. 'So, what are you gonna do about it, lover? Tongues or fingers? It's up to you.' She took his hand, steered him between her legs. 'And you can forget all the hoo-haa this time,' she said. 'Just get down to business.'

TONGUES
(extract from a novel in progress)

CHRISTIN LEE

Out the open car window I watched Venice, sticky, the chatter and commotion gyrating on the walk, tall couples in sun hats, banana-tree overgrowth turning over in the salty breeze, ventilating the alleys. I knew the sweet trash smell lined with jasmine, gasohol vapour and mealy ashes of ganja. Then Danni rolled up the windows and I began to sweat.

I met Danni through my ex. She was peripheral for a while until I started making conversation at parties. When Jack and I were together, she and the others would make laps around him awkwardly. I thought I would make it easy on myself, keep them close, suck it up and fraternise with the ladies in scooped jeans and chucks. Danni was studying Julia Kristeva, Cixous and a group of feminists that I had a fledgling interest in at the time, so I asked question upon question until I clipped the talk and got her another cheap drink.

(Later that year when I made a pass at my theory teacher's boyfriend and the relationship went south, my convictions subsided. My crystal vision of a Third-Wave deluge fell away and became a convolution of misquotations and personal reassurances that my sex life was not getting out of hand. The teacher might never have known about the encounter but I felt some indignity from what I called, at that time, sophisticated guilt. As the Vargas pin-ups came down, display copies of *The Female Eunuch* were put away, the subscription to *On Our Backs* cancelled and the Siouxsie and the Banshees tapes recorded over with Scottish invasion noise-pop, I canned Riot Grrrl camp. Then there was only the din of feminism in the distance and a familiar reminder that, with all the things I cared about, people I liked had loved them first.)

With Danni my reception had usually been cold, wandering eye contact, a locked and senatorial grin, but at a party I once played the sycophant, delivered, 'You look thinner,' across a crowded wet bar and the next week she had already put in a call to me, and a promise that we would be seeing each other sometime soon. I could see she was cold and it wormed into me, grew, took my interest. We met for coffee once and now she had called again. As we drove up Pacific she turned into an unpaved drive and parked along a gutter.

—Hold on, I have to stop in and get sunscreen. I forgot it at home. I knew I was missing something when I was waiting outside, but I didn't want to go in and miss you.

—Again, I'm sorry I was late. Couldn't get my friend off the phone. She's from Minnesota too, actually.

—Yeah?

I followed her into the store, unsure if she had wanted me to stay in the car or continue the conversation. It was crowded with chest-high aisles and one sales counter that sat imposingly near to the sliding-door entrance. Angled from the corner of the laminate ledge a tyre-sized fan pushed warm air in the direction of paying customers, although at that moment, there were none.

—Where?

—Oh, I'm not sure, I just know she has family there, that's all.

She studied the display and rotated each oily bottle to read the print. As Danni worked through the set and the shop clerk gazed on at her, catching a glimpse of her spilling breasts, I walked out and leaned against the portico's pillars. I stared ahead and swiped the sidewalk for interesting people, beautiful people, people who stick in one's vision. One storefront down a pair of men were seated at a table and farther on, past the crispy blue paint peeling off from the wood tiers in sheets, a woman waited for the bus. She was reading. Her head was tilted down toward the leftmost page. I memorised her nose, slight, almost transparent.

The man from the table spoke loudly, like he was trying to get her attention.

—You know things are getting shaky when people from your day are starting to die. I cannot remember a time without these three people . . .

He held up the qualifying fingers. The other man waited.

—Bob Dylan. Barbra Streisand. Ray Charles. Ray Charles, man. It's starting.

The other man shrugged. I looked inside and saw Danni was at the register, rummaging through her purse. She saw me and smiled by squinting her eyes and returned to counting her change. Uninterested in the talk of his red-faced friend, the quieter man stared in the direction of the bus stop and nodded along. The loud man shouted,

—The Irish, man. Over there nobody talks about it, I mean absolutely *nobody*. It's the Roman Catholic thing. Totally cultural.

I couldn't hear the quiet man again.

—No, they won't bring up sex in conversation, I've noticed, they'll talk about it if you bring it up, right. This friend of mine was over here, we're getting to it, and she's, wow, she's taking it way too seriously. I tried to tell her, hon, this is *sports* in America.

Danni walked out and on her arm was a bag heavy and bulging with a generous sampling of suntan lotions. I could still hear the red man as we got back in the car. We drove up the alley and squared the block and in the mirror I could see the quiet man getting smaller.

She was silent for a while and I couldn't tell if she had asked a question or was waiting for mine. Finally Danni said,

—I think you're really going to like Gina. But I want you to know, I respect what you believe. Don't feel pressured into anything.

Danni drew her eyebrows together. I let her off the hook.

—No, I'm here because I'm interested.

—Of course, I'm new to this too.

—How's work?

It kept her busy. She talked about busy until Malibu. She had to. We didn't hit a rhythm, we were polite as mothers, we exchanged easy history back and forth: the facts were just jumping stones to get on, get ahead with the exchange. I was embarrassed too, with every question she asked I seemed to have forgotten my story or lapsed in my own memory. And I was sweating.

—So what about you? Have you seen Jack lately? Since his deal?

I was dizzy with the bars of her serpentine S's. She pushed the crisp sound over like a treadle and it pricked any pocket of interest I could form. I was feeling too small to ask her, could you please turn on the air? Mind if I crack the window? Are you feeling warm? The fog is really burning off. (I could lift my hand and simulate ventilation.) But I laughed instead.

—I've always said, don't date someone you can't avoid.

Boiling like I am? All right if I get some breeze going? AC? This slick coat of sweat is casting me, you have me here, you cannot suffocate yourself toward thinness, it will never come to you this way, I will not be leaving you, you have me here, I am humbled and servile and relinquished and trounced.

—Oh! Ha! That's a shame. I thought it was mutual.

I could only lie.

—Thank you for asking. No, we're fine. We see each other, we're still good friends, really good friends. And you? You're with . . . oh, tall, glasses, the Zionist? I'm sorry—

—Allen, Allen. We broke up. I should say I broke up with him. It's very hard for me. Jack's around though. He's been great – he's been helping me through it.

—Good. That's good.

It was quiet again. She puffed her zoo breasts out and wiggled to lengthen herself, up, up almost out of her tank top, magnificently. Then she pushed her chest on to the steering wheel and levitated her birdlike arms. She asked if she could smoke. I encouraged her and finally rolled down my window. With the flick of a chrome Zippo that had been faithfully handled and rubbed down to a duct-tape grey, she began to tell me about possibility, about ambition, about the pre-tremblings of a life to come. Her life was moments away from her, the award letters, the New York publishing-house calls, the numbers and slipped business cards, op-eds, brunches, private parties at the mouth of Sunset, gift baskets, readings – it was all coming to her. Finally we turned off the highway and coasted down a steep driveway. We parked and she looked up to the mirror.

—I've always been envious of you. Jack and I used to talk about you and I would say how beautiful you are. I hope you know that. Well, thanks for coming today, I knew you were open about these things. That's why I asked you.

—I always hoped we would be friends.

We got out of the car and walked to a beach club. She led me into a dimly lit lobby with low ceilings and a short hall that ended at a desk and two boys whose shirts radiated a white sheen that is associated with luxury cars. We signed a guest book and were handed two identically white towels inscribed with fleurs-de-lis. I walked behind Danni and watched as the hem of her jean shorts stiffly brushed against the firm swathe of skin that depressed beneath her butt with each step. She was flatfooted and didn't swagger, didn't swing, and her ass sat on top of her slim legs more like a flat banana than a set of pears. I felt reassurance. Jack was an ass man.

We walked across the lobby toward the open doors and the scent of sea that had once been lazy was now pungent. The force of the gale made me decide in one moment that I did not regret saying yes to Danni's invitation and that I would try as sincerely as I knew how to enjoy her.

Danni took a few confident steps on to the terrace and as I walked through the square burst of sun I saw a woman looking toward the sea, holding a broad-brimmed sun hat to her head with two hands. Her dress was scrunched in the accordion style that choir ladies and long-waisted women wear so humbly on church patios. I had been warned that she was personable.

—Ladies!

—Gina! This is the friend I told you about.

I was introduced to the woman who was going to teach me glossolalia. As the sun fell through the holes of her hat, Gina's face was dappled by the crosshatch pattern of straw. Her bust looked like a map of varying-sized apertures.

The story of the woman's fortune had been relayed to me on the first invitational phone call. She had lived in Australia, South Africa and the rural margins of Japan for most of her marriage while her scientist husband toured across thirty-four countries with his book, *Fowl Sexing*. He was a turkey-sexer-cum-millionaire. By winning the Zen-Nippon Chick Association's seal of approval, he revolutionised the technique from what had once been, as Gina euphemised, a very impolite matter to one that could determine the sex of a poult within three days of hatching. By breeding an identifiable trait in the female's plume, handlers trained in the old Japanese tradition of sexing were made obsolete and in their place, an indebted niche of farmers grateful that another turkey rectum would never need to be imposed upon again.

—Let's get you ladies fed! Isn't it gorgeous today? Glory be to God!

As we were herded to a buffet line I sensed my own disappointment. She was plain, with small, steady eyes and her cheeks were freckled and moon-boned, but most of all there was nothing unfamiliar about her.

She asked a page to set up chairs and a sunshade closer to the vacant shore and we walked there, shambling through umbrellas and dunes while trying to balance loaded cafeteria trays on our forearms. Gina talked the whole way. We sat down and she said a prayer for the food with closed eyes and fused hands. She invoked the name of Jesus often enough that Danni peeked out from her reverie and stifled a giggle as she caught my attention. Finally, we ate.

Gina finished the story that began on the phone. A short stint in theatre and then an inherited publishing press, small, reputable, and now bequeathed to a daughter freshly divorced. An early retirement in LA.

—Well, I'm just an old church lady now.

Gina laughed, pulled her linen chair around from the picket of umbrellas to face me and closed the circle. She planted the tray in her lap and grasped the armrests of her folding chair with all the force left in her sinewy arms. They looked as if a chamois had been loosely wrapped around a cluster of overripe grapevines. She rubbed her fork between her hands.

—I have to say, I have a sense about you.

I looked at Danni, but Danni was fixed on removing the tomatoes and croutons from her salad.

—I feel the Holy Spirit is telling me that you have suffered a great loss.

—There's nothing that I know of.

—Well, if it doesn't come to you—

—Does he have any leads?

She pulled her chair closer and studied me. She was the kind of woman who made one believe struggle is not permissible.

—Can I say another prayer for us?

She reached out for my hand and I wiped the sweat off my palm before offering it to her. The words tumbled out in the old evangelical style.

—Jesus, we ask for your presence here today, Lord, we ask that you bless this time, Lord, we thank you for our new friend and we pray for her heart, Jesus, that she may be healed by the blood you shed on the Cross, may she find her life in you, Jesus. You brought us here for a purpose, Lord, and we call upon the Holy Spirit to reveal that purpose. Lord Jesus, we also ask for your guidance in revealing our own suffering that perhaps even we are not aware of, Lord, and we bind the enemy in your name, that he will be powerless today, and we pray for freedom from the sin that separates us from you, Lord Jesus Christ. Amen.

I had been holding my breath, and as I released it I spilled my drink on to the sand. I tried to distract them.

—Really, I can't think of anything. Thank you for your concern, but it's unnecessary.

—Why don't you take a look at this?

She handed me a tract-sized booklet whose paper cover was striped in red and pink with an abstract square that may have been a house on fire, or a bisected birthday cake. In flaming lettering, *Why Tongues?* was printed and underlined with a thick white stripe.

—Why don't you take a look at that while Danni tells you about her prayer language? Is that OK, Danni?

Danni was adjusting her bra strap. She looked up quickly and nodded, took another bite, puffed out her chest and collected herself. She told me that she had first learned to speak in tongues by making small baby noises, vowel sounds, morphemes, and now she prayed in tongues every day. She told me she didn't know what she was saying, but sometimes it made her cry. I put this inside the frame of our other encounters and was almost sure she was lying.

—So you don't understand what your language is saying. Then – I don't mean to be rude, this is all very interesting to me – but how do you know that you're saying anything at all?

Gina interceded.

—No, please ask questions! We love them! Right? God wants us to ask questions.

—Yes.

—I can tell you are a very bright, very wise woman. You have a presence about you, I can tell just by sitting here with you. A strong presence.

—Well, thank you.

And then Danni, who raised one hand absent-mindedly and smacked her thumb against her fingers like a moving mouth, explained the complexities of a Divine Body in three parts whose Spirit speaks through the voices of the saved.

I had decided I wanted to hear them. I glanced at the headings of the tract: 'The Bible's Way to Receive the Holy Spirit', 'Ten Reasons why Every Believer Should Speak in Tongues'. One reason suggested 'Praying in Tongues Enables Us to Pray for the Unknown'.

I was feeling light-headed. Back and forth they accompanied their testimonies with truths and verses and doctrines that rang with the stately cantilena of myth while I was silent and nodding along, trying to remember when I had stopped going to church and started reading poetry. We make monsters to understand things! God's existence has been a crapshoot since Copernicus! Follow your idea of eternity and you will see it is more frightening than what is already inside of you! I couldn't think of a way to take up the conversation again and it looked as if they were each waiting for the other to broach the question. Finally Gina said,

—It looks like we're finished eating. Why don't we go someplace more private?

We shuffled back to the club in silence and stopped in front of a long line of cabanas. Gina unlocked the façade and threw the doors open to reveal a faux tiki hut. She invited us to take a seat on a couch embroidered with toucans and obligingly we sat under a low ceiling where starfish hung like turncoats.

We faced the sea and, as the world stood then, we were alone and heralded in the distance by the shrieks of children.

—Do you think you'd like to join us?

—No, thank you, not yet.

—You're sure?

—I think I'll listen, though, for me that would be helpful. If you didn't mind?

They bowed their heads. Gina began.

—Lord Jesus Christ, we thank you for the bounty of this day, for your edification and ours. Christ . . .

And on, and Danni,

—Amen, amen.

—We call upon the Holy Spirit in your name, Christ Jesus.

They were quiet for a minute. And then they went there, to the place I couldn't follow.

Snowfall
(opening of a novel)

KATY MCAULAY

Nathan

When it first started the five people at Nathan's dinner party had laughed. They moved to press noses to cold glass, and the girl from Australia, who had never seen snow before, ran down the winding flights of stairs and out into the street where she stood with her head tilted back and arms flung wide to the sky, the way she had seen them do in films.

On the third night, after the street lights went out and the Australian girl disappeared, Yvonne washed the last of the dishes in her brother's kitchen and distributed candles to the strangers who lived in his building, using the temporary goodwill that emergency situations can lend you.

But listen. By the seventh day, when Nathan hugged his sister and forced a way out into the white to search for his girlfriend Laura, the city was suffocating under its downy pillow. Archie was dead and the others had felt the shift in temperature in the people around them, had felt it in themselves, as they plummeted to numb cold.

Glasgow is not routinely admired for its beauty, and the first clouds, hanging artless and pregnant in the sky, are not aware

of the splendour they are creating. The flakes do not discrim-
inate. They land on the brothels and the churches, the squat-
ting red tenements and the silent financial sector. They fall on
the metal shell of the IMAX cinema and the half-restored
glasshouses in the Botanical Gardens. Urban gulls, cruising
the blocks for that opening stab at abandoned kebabs, are the
first to notice the flakes softening the black patent roofs.
Flurries finger the curves of a stone angel waiting high on the
rooftops of Sauchiehall Street. Snow settles on ornate win-
dowsills too far above the ground to be appreciated, and, not
satisfied, nestles further into windows sticky with city smog.

A little further down, flakes cling to the takeaway signs
and slip along the huge neon chopsticks above the Noodle
Bar, melting and refreezing with each blast of curry-flavoured
air that escapes its swinging door. Inside, a Japanese girl has
climbed on to the wide counter to shout order numbers and
marshal the hungry throng while taxis queue to take the early
Friday night drunks home with signs on their door that say
NO EATING AND DRINKING IN THIS CAB. Just before they touch
the street, some of the snowflakes can be thrown back
skywards by the shrieks of a hen party teetering across the
tarmac or a punch of music from the entrance of a packed
bar, before the bouncers, who have stepped aside to admit
shivering women, shut the door and seal the heat back in.

Snow falls at the feet of beautiful people, bantering and
gesticulating in queues for the right nightclub, while on
another corner a different kind of beautiful people also wait.
Sullen against railings, they blink slowly, dislodging delicate
flakes from their mascaraed eyelashes.

Already the white patterns have hypnotised drivers into a smash by the dark river. They have broken up a fistfight on Jamaica Street. Next to the shadowed arches of Central Station, a thief makes use of the diversion to slide a cold hand into a pocket and grasp the wallet there, while on Bath Street, Casanovas use the dip in temperature as an excuse to clasp exposed skin and kiss upturned faces. The rumbling underfoot caused by the subway trains pushing stale air in a circle has ceased for the night, but in this city something is always happening just below the surface. The next man, the next woman, the next band, the next fight, the next hit: they are all of them just around the corner.

As clutches of people emerge, wobbly-legged as fawns, out of the city's cellar bars to blink and gasp at the spectacle of the early snowfall, Nathan has stepped into this quieter, mostly asleep street to see the flat white flakes fall cool as blades on the Australian girl's face. He is full and drunk and happy.

'Nathan!'

Thwock.

Balled-up snow slaps him wetly in the head. Slivers slip and dribble down his neck as his sister cackles and ducks back inside. It's not quite sticking on the pavement yet, so he scoops two handfuls from a nearby windshield and crouches by the low wall, eyes trained on the door.

Yvonne comes barrelling out so fast that his first shot is wide of the mark but he manages to corner her as she attempts to hurdle the wall. Squishes the other handful gently against her face. She giggles and protests breathlessly.

'Truce! Truce! Agh!'

The Australian girl has not broken her dramatic pose. Without a coat, her knees are turning pink. She opens her eyes wide and says, to no one and to everyone, 'It's so beautiful.'

A prickle at the back of his neck makes Nathan look up at his flat. In the window, Archie is looking down at the Australian girl, a frown on his pale face. Nathan watches Laura tug Archie's sleeve, mouthing something, and the pair move away from the glass.

A year earlier, a stranger told Nathan that Laura was the right girl for him before he had ever even met her. Waiting for the barman to fix him a Jack and Coke, he wasn't prepared for the short young woman with the auburn curls and milky skin who detached herself from her friends and marched towards him.

'Can I get your phone number?'

'What?'

'I said, can I get your phone number?'

'Um. Haven't you been kissing that guy over there for most of the night?'

'It's not for me. It's for my flatmate.' She smiled impishly. Her pupils were wide, from drink or the darkness of the bar, he wasn't sure.

'Which one is your flatmate?'

'She's not here.'

'Three pounds,' said the barman.

'She's not here?' The smooth-skinned girl shook her curls. 'Thanks.' He swirled the wedge of lime around the glass to buy some time. 'Well then, how do you know that she wants my number?'

'You're just her type. She has this thing for blond guys,' the imp said, and he smiled then, in spite of himself.

'How can you be sure that I'll like *her*?' he asked.

'Oh, *you'll like her.*' A fast song came on then and her small feet swivelled towards the sweating bodies on the dance floor. She began to bob her head in time to the beat. Nathan thought quickly.

'What's her name?'

'Laura.'

He took a swig of his drink, the ice clunking against his teeth. 'OK,' he said. 'Give me Laura's number and I'll call her.'

'I'm not handing out my friend's number to a man she doesn't even know.' Her eyes twinkled at him.

'I won't give you my number,' he said. 'Give me *her* number and I promise I'll call.'

A week later, on the 5th of November, he found the imp waiting for him under the running-clock statue beside the bus station. She was dressed like a flapper, with a large bloom tied around her wrist, and her pale skin smelled of strawberries, though winter had just begun.

Nathan, Yvonne and the coatless Australian girl are standing in the middle of the road, their three pink tongues stuck straight out, quivering into the sharp air. They are attempting to catch snowflakes. He is a little thin, Nathan. Not scrawny, exactly, but he gives the impression of not quite having finished growing, even though he is twenty-eight. It could be the years spent crouched under a spotlight scribbling away at his architecture degree that did it, but he has a certain bright-eyed, undernourished look that makes girls smile at him and women want to feed him spoonfuls of hot stew.

Now his mouth is stained with red wine and his eyes are filled with spiralling puffs of white. Traffic whispers to him in the distance. The Australian girl is twirling slowly, keeping step with the turning of the earth. A snowflake drops to rest on his outstretched tongue. It sits proudly for a moment, twinkles, droops and disappears.

The Australian girl curls her body over the bonnet of a parked car and vomits into the gutter.

'I'm sorry,' she mumbles, 'I'm really sorry,' and Nathan and Yvonne guide her inside, exchanging glances over her bowed head.

Laura has fallen asleep on the sofa and Archie is picking at the remains of the carved chicken on the table. He looks agitated. Nathan sheds his coat and Archie says, 'The cheesecake was melting, so I put it back in the freezer.' Nathan makes a face. 'I don't think any of us will want any,' he says. 'How long has Laura been asleep?'

'Not long. Maybe five minutes.'

Nathan perches carefully next to her and strokes her hair. She snuffles a little and smiles.

'Laura. Laura?'

'Mmmmh . . .'

'Laura, do you want to get into bed?'

'Dathan?' she says, her voice thick and husky with a cold. 'Oh. Doh.' She shakes her head. 'I feel awful. I think I should go hombe.'

'You can stay here if you like. I'll make you a hot-water bottle?' He puts his hand on her forehead. She shifts, dislodging him, and opens her eyes. 'Doh,' she says. 'I'm too hotdh. And I wouldh feel badh if you got id.' She pulls herself up and sits, looking into the fire.

In the bedroom he tries again while she finds her coat. 'It's snowing pretty hard out there.'

'I'll be fined.' She fumbles with the buttons and then takes her gloves off to fasten them. He feels for her hands.

'You still haven't given me an answer.'

'I said I'd be OK.'

'I don't mean about that.' Her hands agitate to get back to the buttons on her coat. 'I doh,' she says. 'I'm thinkingh about id.' He runs his fingers over her palm, pulls gently at her fingers.

'Dathan. I *am* thinkingh about id.'

'I'm just saying. Your lease runs out soon. Think more.'

There's a shy knock on the door and Archie pokes his nose into the room. 'Hello? Sorry. Hi.'

'Archie, it's fine, come in,' says Nathan.

'Sorry,' Archie repeats. 'Do you have any cloths? She's been sick again. I'm sorry about this, man. If I'd known she would be this way, I never would have brought her.'

'It's all right,' says Nathan. 'Cupboard under the sink. Where is she now?'

'Passed out in the spare room.'

'OK. She can stay here. Just let her sleep it off.' Archie looks at him, relieved and grateful. 'You want to stay too?' Nathan asks.

'Um. N . . . no. I think I should go home. Besides, someone should really walk Laura.' They nod at each other.

'OK.'

Laura dabs gently at the chafed skin around her nose. 'She's a bid drabatic, isn'd she?' she says. 'I meandh. It's only snow.' Archie pulls on his coat. 'Are you two . . .' she asks, and Nathan shoots her a glance, 'together?'

Archie pulls up his collar. 'Eh . . . no,' he says. 'No, I don't think so.'

The snow has hidden the foul patterns of the Australian girl's vomit and now it settles into the footsteps of Archie and Laura. Slowly, it muffles cold cars. Quietly, it brushes against the window of Nathan's living room.

Inside, Nathan uses a broken foot pump to inflate a mattress for his little sister to sleep on.

Eeek-eeek-eeek-eeek-eeek-eeek.

Yvonne has gone to the bathroom to brush her teeth and the flat is quiet. In the living room, Nathan is tiring of the pump.

Eeeeeek. Eeeeeeek.

'Sounds like you're torturing a mouse.'

Puffed, he pauses for a moment and watches Yvonne pad into the room wearing pyjamas. She lets down her thick hair. 'I would have done that,' she says. But he's glad of the exertion provided by the broken pump, hopes it might make his eyelids heavy enough to beat his active mind. These days he doesn't sleep well without Laura's limbs to curve his self around. You probably know exactly how he feels. When you've met it in a good mood, the city can catch you up into the swing and waltz of a thousand others. And yet, when the morning has not yet broken, and the birds you never notice in the day are clamouring in the parks, insubstantiality can sneak in.

You need something to push your body against then. For some, the comforts of a music collection, the routine of a smoke before bedtime or the steady breathing of another body can do it. Nathan has found something better. Better than even his beloved buildings. Better than the imagined bridges that wait in the wings to be designed as he draws plans for office refits.

'How's it going, little sis?'

'Not bad, big bruv.'

'This do you?'

'Suits me just fine.' She slides into the slippy folds of the sleeping bag.

'How is stuff?' he asks her. 'Work? Is it any better?'

'About the same. Parties and press releases.' She smiles, embarrassed.

'Dad told me about the promotion. Hey, you must be doing something right.'

'Yeah. I know. I'm really quite good at it.' She frowns. 'It's just . . . Ach, it's probably nothing, I just feel a bit . . .'

'A bit . . .? Down?'

'No. Not that. Restless.'

Through the wall, the Australian girl shifts and murmurs and behind thin curtains, the snow continues to drift down, silent and forgotten as falling leaves.

CONTRIBUTORS' NOTES

George Anderson was born in Twechar in 1966. He has worked in journalism and wildlife conservation, and is also a musician. His story 'Tumshie McFadgen's Bid for Ultimate Bliss' was adapted into a BAFTA-winning film of the same name.

Kirsten Anderson was born in Kilmarnock. She is twenty-eight. She lived and studied in Edinburgh for a few years, but has lived in Glasgow since 2002.

Fiona Bingham is twenty-three and grew up in Sheffield, South Yorkshire. She currently lives in Stirling.

Felix Boon lives in Glasgow. The novel *Filling in the Blanks* is being written under the influence of Edward Said and Hélène Cixous. Set in Glasgow, it looks at asylum seekers, identity and the representation of 'others.'

Sara Bryce has taught English in Japan and has a black belt in shorinji kempo.

Ann Burnett has taught in Canada, Australia and Scotland. She writes scripts for BBC schools' and children's radio and TV, and is now writing for adults.

Lorna Callery is a Glasgow-based artist and writer.

Allison Deeds was born and raised in Cleveland, Ohio, and graduated with a BA in English from Baldwin-Wallace College. She spent a year working in Ireland and Scotland and has returned to Glasgow.

Kate Dowd is twenty-two and comes from the American Midwest. She graduated in 2005 with a BA in English literature from Gonzaga University and plans to work towards a PhD.

Ewan Gault was born in 1981. He is currently working on a collection of short stories.

Alison Irvine was born in London. She has worked as an actress and a medical secretary. She is working on a novel.

Christin Lee is twenty-three and was born and raised in California. She is a graduate of Loyola Marymount University.

John Mc Geown was born in 1982 and grew up in Newry, County Down. He has lived in Dublin for the past five years.

Katy McAulay is a freelance journalist and writer based in Glasgow. Her short stories have appeared in the *Scotsman* and *Product* magazine. She is twenty-four.

Andrea McNicoll was born in Scotland. She lived in Asia for fourteen years. Based in Edinburgh now, she has just completed her first book: a series of interwoven stories set in rural Thailand.

Anneliese Mackintosh is twenty-three. She grew up in Buckinghamshire and graduated from the University of Nottingham in 2003 with a degree in English studies. She now lives and studies in Glasgow.

Marie-Anne Mancio was born in London. She has a doctorate in live art and critical theory.

Theresa Muñoz was born in Vancouver, Canada. Her work has appeared in *The Claremont Review, Room of One's Own* and *Canadian Literature*.

Allan Radcliffe was born in Perth. He has worked as a teacher and a journalist and lives in Edinburgh. His articles, short stories and poems have appeared in *The Sunday Times, Scotsman, Sunday Herald, Celtic View, List, Metro* and *Big Issue*. His monologue *When the Moon Was Overhead* will be performed at the Hunterian Art Gallery, Glasgow, in September 2006 and the Walker Gallery, Liverpool, in January 2007. He is currently working on a novel.

Hannah Ritchie grew up in Inverness and now lives in Glasgow. She is currently writing a novel set in both cities.

Alastair Sim has published short stories, play scripts and the novel *Rosslyn Blood* (see www.rosslynblood.com). His second novel, *Bàn*, is a Hebridean thriller of drugs and the occult, and he is writing a Victorian detective novel, *The Unbelievers*. He is represented by literary agent Jane Conway-Gordon, 1 Old Compton Street, London W1D 5JA.

Mary Smith, after working in Pakistan and Afghanistan, returned to Dumfries and Galloway where she works as a freelance journalist.

Eleanor Thom was born in 1979. She has a degree in French and Italian and a Masters in linguistics. She has worked as a historic building conservationist, a linguistics researcher and a nanny, and has lived in London, Paris and Turin. Now living in Glasgow, she is writing a novel based on family myths and recollections.

Maggie Walker moved from the west coast of England to the west coast of Scotland in 2002. She writes poetry and stories and is completing her first novel.

Vincent Wells lives in Glasgow and is working on a novel.

Les Wood has had several short stories published as well as some poetry, and was a winner of the 2002 Canongate Prize for New Writing and a prizewinner in the 2004 McCash Scots Poetry competition. In his day job he is a senior lecturer in human physiology at Glasgow Caledonian University.